The H

ui

Zombie Forensics
and
Medicine

The Handbook of Zombie Forensics and Medicine

A New Theory of Zombiology and Why Humans Will (Probably) Survive the Apocalypse

By

Darin L. Wolfe, M.D.

Dedication

This book is dedicated to my parents,
who always supported my aspirations
but probably let me watch too many
scary movies as a child.

"The dead shall live; their corpses shall rise.
Awake and sing, ye that dwell in the dust:
for the dew is as the dew of herbs,
and the earth shall give birth to her dead."
— Isaiah 26:19

The Handbook of Zombie Forensics and Medicine

Table of Contents

Introduction:

When the White Horse Rides

In the Book of Revelation, it is said that the Four Horsemen of the Apocalypse represent War (The Red Horse), Famine (The Black Horse), Plague (The White Horse) and Death (The Pale Horse). There have been times in history when many thought the White Horse had finally ridden out, leaving apocalyptic pestilence in its wake. In 1918-1919, the Spanish influenza spread over the world, killing approximately 50 million people with its severe and unusual symptoms in previously healthy patients. In 1346, the Black Death (bubonic plague) emerged in Europe and is estimated to have killed up to 200 million people in the four years of its dark reign. Despite devastating effects on the population, we as a species survived and even thrived in the wake of these terrible scourges. But the White Horse is again restless.

Infectious disease experts say that we are long overdue for a cataclysmic disease to finally emerge and threaten the very existence of humanity. The conditions have never been better for a truly apocalyptic infection that could kill billions and even trigger War, Famine and ultimately the Death of humankind. Emerging infectious diseases are being discovered at an alarming rate. The population is growing faster than we are dying off, causing crowding all around the world. The ease of global travel can bring deadly sicknesses to distant shores in under a day's time. But as scientists train their eyes on

1

things like Asian bird flu and tropical hemorrhagic fever viruses, could the apocalypse arise from something entirely *human* in origin?

Could humanity meet its fate by way of *zombies*?

The surprising and unsettling answer is "Yes", but perhaps not in the way you might think. On the surface this seems like a silly suggestion. Zombies are just corpses that rise from the dead only to be battered, chopped and shot up by humans, right? As it turns out, zombiology is a little more complex than this outdated depiction. In this book, the usual iteration of the resurrected dead type zombies will be extensively dissected and redefined. But more relevant to apocalyptic candidates, we ask the question, "Could a disease arise in the *living* that produces a syndrome with no functional differences from the zombies we see in pop culture lore?" Even more unsettling, could such a disease actually be more dangerous than what has been depicted? It is upon answering these questions that we introduce a new theory of zombiology in which living zombies are defined within the parameters of what is known about clinical medicine, forensic pathology, infectious disease and physiology.

We understand the great controversy this will stir within the growing field of zombiology, but it is our position that a full understanding of the major zombie types is essential if humankind is to survive an apocalyptic outbreak. In the following pages, we will delve deeply into the science of zombiology, paying homage to the zombies of the past while hypothesizing and preparing for the zombies of the future. Before going forward you must release from your mind any preconceived notions about zombies that you might have learned from *The Walking Dead*, *Night of the Living Dead* or the *Thriller* music video. As it turns out, zombies are much more complex than the rotting, brain-eating creatures we've been told about. No matter what walks of life we come from or our educational backgrounds, we must all become zombiologists to defeat this threat when the White Horse finally rides out from the shadows.

PART I:

Modern Zombiology & The Diagnosis of Death

One of the questions I am often asked is, "Why would you work so hard to go to medical school only to choose a career surrounded by dead people?" It is true that medicine is a noble career focused on the cure of the living and relief from suffering. But as it turns out, being an expert in disease, death and decomposition is excellent preparation for the field of **zombiology**, the study of zombies and the disease of zombiism. Most medical students can point to a seminal moment during his or her education when it became clear which medical specialty to choose. For me, the path to becoming a forensic pathologist/zombiologist began during an unusual patient encounter during the first night on call at the beginning of my 3rd year of medical school.

It was the beginning of June and I had just begun my service for one of the Internal Medicine teams at a busy hospital in downtown Indianapolis. The medicine clerkship was a well-known challenge for new medical students because the wards were packed with some of the sickest and most complex patients in the city. I had spent most of that first week roaming the cavernous, century-old brick hospital, chasing down lab results and continually checking on the three patients that I had been assigned. My once crisp-looking short white coat was now dusty on the elbows and sleeves. The pockets were overstuffed with notecards, ink pens and a folded stethoscope. The hours were long and the learning curve was very steep, but on this particular summer evening I would finally get some solo responsibility during my first night on-call. It turned out to be a terrifying experience, but one that would provide inspiration for my eventual career choice.

My role as the "on-call" junior medical student was to help evaluate new patients in the Emergency Department. I expected patients with infections, kidney stones or minor injuries but as it turned out, my first patient encounter would offer one of the most shocking and aggressive patients of my career. Although, I must tell you that since I eventually became a forensic pathologist, any living and breathing patient would be both shocking and aggressive in my line of work.

All was quiet for the first three hours after my shift began. I sat alone at a computer station on the 4th floor, writing progress notes and looking up lab results for my patients. My pager went off, rattling loudly as it pulsated on the desktop next to the computer. I recognized the callback number from the Emergency Department, grabbed my stethoscope and raced down a poorly lit stairwell. It was a dull gray concrete shaft with badly worn steps, flickering lights and heavy steel doors that took considerable effort to push open. My heart was pumping hard when I reached the bottom floor.

I took a moment to catch my breath then proceeded to the main desk where the triage nurse awaited me. Nurse Ratcliff seemed to have a kind of serene indifference at the chaos around us: clipboards were flying, orders were being barked across hallways and nurses, respiratory therapists, EMTs and various folks in white coats darted in and out of rooms. Family members and other loved ones of sick patients were making their agitation well known to anyone who would listen. I suspect I must have looked as if though my face was melting off, because she instantly homed in on me[1].

"Medical student?" she asked.

"Yes. Internal Medicine, team Yellow…Name is Wolfe." I said.

On the counter in front of her was a metal rack of clipboards, each one representing a current patient in the ED. There was a sheet of basic information including name and gender, age and the Chief Complaint—the reason the patient was there. Nurse Ratcliff snatched a clipboard and handed it to me.

"Your patient is Mr. Garcia, a 49 year old male. Have fun with this one. He's in Holding."

"Holding?" I repeated.

"Yesssss." She drew out the syllable and raised one eyebrow over the rim of her glasses. I had no idea what she was talking about. A nearby doctor must have seen me looking utterly glazed over. Her badge read, "Dr. Valenta, Intern".

"It means he's at a high risk of violence or escape." She said.

She grabbed the clipboard from my hand and skimmed it quickly, furrowing her brow as she scanned the face sheet.

"Looks like he was transferred here from the prison…attacked a prison guard and had been acting strangely for at least a day. I'd order a full chem panel, CBC and maybe a chest X-ray and head CT. Should probably get a Psych consult as well."

She tossed the clipboard back to me, grabbed her own chart and disappeared into a patient's room before I had a chance to ask any questions. I read Mr. Garcia's summary

---

[1] Seasoned nurses can sense fear.

sheet, which included his vital signs and the reason why he had been brought in:

*"***Chief Complaint:*** Altered Mental Status".*

Although this is a generic term that can cover an array of symptoms, it meant he was

disoriented and based on what Dr. Valenta had said, possibly combative.

The excitement of getting my first patient decayed into anxiety and uncertainty. Gone

were the days of the quiet clinics of my first two years of medical school. As I made my

way through the deepest recesses of the ED to find the Holding area, I tried to formulate

the differential diagnosis for what could be causing his problems. Generally, the causes

of altered mental status include things like drug or alcohol intoxication but could also

include poisoning, infections and diseases of the brain.

I knew I had finally found the Holding area when I saw two uniformed men with badges

and guns standing in front of a large black door with chipped paint and a small square

window near the top.

"Which one you here for?" said the guard as he loomed over me.

"Mr. Garcia." I said, as I handed him the clipboard.

He looked at my identification badge, then at the chart.

"Yeah, *that* guy. Sheesh." He exhaled and shook his head as he poked the keypad

security code buttons. The door unlocked with a dull metallic '*clack*'.

"Good luck with that one." he said, as I brushed past him.

My experience in medicine is that when someone wishes you "luck" or to "have fun",

that usually means "*I am really glad I am not in your shoes right now.*"

The room's beds were arranged in a semi-circle, each one separated by a thin curtain. I

approached Mr. Garcia to begin my history and physical exam. On the gurney before me lay a thin but muscular man with long black hair. He was clad in a bright orange jumpsuit and his wrists and ankles were secured to the metal bed frame with leather restraints. His eyes were tightly closed and his chest was rapidly rising and falling with each breath.

I wondered how I would even take a history or do a physical exam. During the first two years of medical school I learned the ins and outs of pretty much every disease and the underlying cellular pathology and biochemistry that defined it. But I had no experience with an undiagnosed, nonverbal and aggressive patient.

His face and neck appeared strained, making every muscle fiber and tendon seem like rubbery cords stretched beneath his skin. His brow was creased and beaded with sweat and his hair was matted. He seemed to be in a trance-like state while he mumbled unintelligible words and quivered. I stood at the foot of his bed unsure what to do next.

"Mister…Garcia?" I said quietly.

He grimaced and retracted his lips over his gray-black gums, revealing several broken and misshapen yellow teeth.

"Mister Garcia, I'm going to examine you now."

We were trained to address every patient the same way but my words to Mr. Garcia felt useless. He grunted and began to open and close his hands as if firmly grasping and releasing something. He made low, guttural moans that seemed to grow louder as I drew closer. I reached into my pocket and pulled out a penlight and gently retracted one of his eyelids and shone the light in. He roared with eardrum-bursting volume and hissed as he arched his back. This was photophobia, an extreme sensitivity and pain upon seeing light. An exhalation of noxious gases was forced from his lungs and filled the space around him with an unbearable stench that was like rotting flesh. His entire body twisted and slammed against the bed, rattling the metal rails and drawing the attention of everyone nearby. He then opened his eyes widely and fixed his gaze on me with a look that conveyed a desperate, murderous rage. His entire torso bucked toward me violently and I began to wonder if the restraints were going to be enough to keep him in place. He yelled out again and this gave way to a spell of coughing so violent that blood began to spew from his lips onto his jumpsuit and the bed around him. A nurse and a resident physician ran over to help and he was quickly given a sedative to calm him. I backed away from Mr. Garcia feeling both terrified and defeated. My first patient was an enigma.

***

On first glance, there was no discernible cause for Mr. Garcia's altered mental state but one thing was evident: His mind had been at least temporarily stripped away. He had become animalistic, uncontrollable and violent. As I watched him writhe and bare his teeth and use flesh-ripping force to try and break his restraints, I could only think of one word to describe him: zombie.

Even thinking that word seemed a bit disrespectful. I had been trained to approach every patient the same way and treat all humanely. He was a man, not a monster, of course. The term 'zombie' is often used in a flippant or even derogatory sense when describing a human being, but how different was this man from the depictions we have seen of the zombies from pop culture? He did not demonstrate any cognitive ability nor did he speak. He postured aggressively while in the Holding area and had previously attacked a prison guard. Even his physical examination was suggestive of a zombie-like disease: He had bloodshot eyes and profound photophobia, moaned with his mouth agape and he had many broken teeth. A smell like death was all around. But Mr. Garcia was very much alive as was indicated by his markedly elevated heart and breathing rates and extreme agitation.

Fortunately for Mr. Garcia (and the world), his condition was not infectious. After numerous lab tests of the blood and imaging studies of his body, it was found that he had liver failure due to cirrhosis. The liver had lost the ability to effectively filter waste products from his bloodstream, one of which was ammonia (NH_3). The elevated ammonia levels began to have a toxic effect on his brain, producing a condition called "hepatic encephalopathy". The word 'hepatic' refers to liver and '**encephalopathy**' means a disease of the brain in which function is altered by a toxin or infection.

Mr. Garcia was transferred to the Intensive Care Unit (ICU) for medical therapy to improve his liver function and to help remove the wastes from his bloodstream. About 48 hours later, as the ammonia levels returned to near normal, Mr. Garcia's aggressive behavior disappeared, his muscles relaxed and he finally opened his eyes without pain. After several days in the hospital, he was able to speak coherently, walk and eat. His clinical condition had been explained and treated medically and he had returned to his baseline "normal". Prior to his discharge from the hospital I was able to conduct some follow-up questions with him. I talked to him plainly about his condition and he had a very pleasant demeanor. He told me that he had absolutely no memory of anything over the last week.

"What *do* you remember before you came to the hospital?" I asked.

He seemed to stare off past me as he began to talk.

"The last thing I remember was sitting in my cell, feeling very angry. It was just like, this demon inside of me. I couldn't shake it, and I just felt angrier and angrier. I was pounding my fists against walls until they bled. I had no idea why I was doing it. It just kept building. I don't remember attacking the guard. I have no memory of any of it."

Mr. Garcia was discharged in fairly good condition, although he would have to contend with his continued liver failure to prevent future episodes of encephalopathy. A few weeks later, I completed my duties on Internal Medicine clerkship and moved on to a different hospital. I would neither see Mr. Garcia in a follow-up clinic visit nor ever again, but the experience stayed with me.

The Garcia case represented the moment that made me think differently about the word "zombie". Our aggressive impulses have mostly been hidden by millions of years of higher brain development but can bubble to the surface under the right conditions. I reflected deeply on this case and about how beneath our façade of civility, there is still a mostly dormant core of functions that center around aggression, anger and attack. This revelation has become the fracture point in the world of zombiology: It was conceivable that a *living* person could manifest intensely violent and irrational behavior if a chemical (toxin or drug) or infectious agent could affect the areas of the brain that govern aggression and impulse control. Zombies were no longer just creatures rising from death to attack the living.

Mr. Garcia's case was a kind of 'biochemical zombiism' involving ammonia as the causative agent. **Zombiism** (zom-bee-izm), is defined as zombie-like behavior and related clinical symptoms. Although Mr. Garcia's condition responded to treatment and he returned to his old self, what if his symptoms had been persistent and unable to be reversed? Even more intriguing, what if those symptoms were reproducible in another individual via an infectious organism? These are the concepts that underlie the basis for modern zombiology.

Do not fret about the dead. The classical zombies—the dead ones—are also still very much a part of the study of zombiology and will be extensively profiled in this text. But before we get too deeply into the differences between the zombie types we must review some of the basic tenets that govern zombies, the Zombie Axioms. These simple statements aim to put us all on equal footing to understand the threat we will face when a zombiism outbreak eventually occurs. The Axioms will also serve as a basis for the division of the Dead and the Living zombies into their appropriate subtypes.

The Zombie Axioms, Zombie Types & Nomenclature

The Zombie Axioms are statements formulated by our research group with respect to the current scientific knowledge of zombiism.

Axiom 1:   The zombie is a creature that has human form, is genetically human, and was at some point in the past both neurologically and physically intact but has lost the higher cognitive functions and reasoning ability of the human brain.

Axiom 2:   The zombie demonstrates aggressive interpersonal behavior and attacking tendencies toward normal (non-zombie) humans but may or may not include cannibalism.

Axiom 3:   The zombie may be caused by an infectious biological agent, chemical or may be **idiopathic** (cause not known).

Axiom 4:   The zombie may or may not have clinical death prior to classic zombie-like behavior.

Axioms 1-3 are accepted by most modern zombiologists and include both the classic risen dead and the living zombies, but Axiom 4 has become the dividing line in the world of zombiology. The 'old' zombie definition maintains the person has to have died prior to exhibiting zombiism symptoms; in our classification system this is known as a **Type 1 zombie**. There are many names still in use for this type of zombie, including *classical zombiism, Old World zombiism* or simply *the Resurrected Dead (RD)*. These terms are used interchangeably throughout the book and likely will be in public use until the World Health Organization (WHO) holds a congress on the zombiism disease.

For those that accept Axiom 4, the patient has not necessarily suffered clinical death but exhibits symptoms of zombie-like behavior. These are referred to as **Type 2** zombies, just as Mr. Garcia would have been considered if his condition were persistent and irreversible. Type 2 zombiism patients are infected with a pathogenic microorganism (such as a virus, bacterium, prion etc.) or are under the influence of some other non-biological agent (such as a drug, chemical or electromagnetic signal, etc.). These zombies have been said to be afflicted with *New World Zombiism or Neo-zombiism.*

Over the last decade and a half of zombie studies, the concept of the 'living zombie' has gained favor and credibility. Even the Merriam-Webster dictionary makes a provision for the zombie definition to include "a person held *to resemble* the so-called walking dead" and "a person in markedly strange appearance and behavior". For the general population, definitions and diagnostic nomenclature may not seem to matter much if we wake up one morning to find there are aggressive humanoid hordes attacking our cities and causing chaos and death.

As we go forward through the subject of zombiology, the importance of Axiom 4 cannot be overstated. The living and dead zombies are very different biologically and these differences have huge implications for quarantine and treatment possibilities, legal implications and even the kind of weapons you may choose for defense. Being well prepared and knowing which type you are dealing with will promote your survival and the victory over the disease outbreak.

The Diagnosis of Death: The Key Feature of Zombie Subtype

The discipline of modern zombiology demands that we accurately diagnose death, as this is the key element that differentiates the Type 1 (Resurrected Dead) and Type 2 (Living) zombies. While there are many death-specific tests that rely on advanced technology, the regular citizens in the midst of a zombie outbreak may have to make the death determination themselves, and without the aid of a CT scanner or EEG machine. To the uninitiated, the death diagnosis seems obvious. That is, until you have to do it yourself on a freshly dead body.

The Death Exam of Mr. Gray

In the small hours of an August morning, I struggled to maintain wakefulness after another night on call. I gazed into the dark abyss of the computer screen. The contrast of the bright orange letters and numbers on the black screen burned my eyes, which were already weary after having been on shift for the past 16 hours. But the hectic afternoon-to-midnight flurry of patients had passed. The hospital had grown quiet and my mind settled into a place of placid fatigue. Then at around 2:30am, my pager emitted its high-pitched scream and vibrated on my belt. I felt my heart thump in my chest as I dialed the callback number. On the line was the voice of the senior resident, Dr. Armstrong. He asked me a most unusual question.

"Hey...you ever do a death exam?" He said.

"I, uh...no?" I said. I was perplexed.

Medical school was about examining and treating the living, so of course I had not performed a 'death exam'. I didn't even know what that meant.

"Meet me up on 3 West ward in 10 minutes. We had a man die."

Medical school could be described as a series of events in which the student persists in a state of confused obedience. As such, I rushed from my work area on a different ward to the nurse's station on a medical ward in the East wing. At this time of night, the halls were quiet and the lights were turned down to promote rest for the sick and weary patients. Only the asynchronous beeps of distant heart monitors punctuated the silence. A figured emerged from one of the rooms, a slim man with short auburn hair and wire-rimmed glasses. His white coat gave him an almost ghostly appearance in the darkness of the hallway. He extended his hand and waved me toward him and then made a pointing motion to a room on his right. I made my way down the hall.

"This is Mr. Gray. He died about an hour ago. There isn't an official note in the chart so you're doing the Death Exam." He said.

Thanks...I guess?

I entered the room and immediately noticed the absence of sound. No beeping monitors. No shifting movements in the bed. No television. No breathing. It was a different kind of quiet, like the silent tension of a held breath. Only the curtain before me concealed the body of Mr. Gray. Dr. Armstrong whipped the curtain back with a grating metallic *scriiitch* sound that caused me to jump a little in my shoes. Mr. Gray lay supine before me. I was about to see and touch the first 'freshly dead' human body in my life and in the process confirm his clinical death. This wasn't like the cadaver from the Gross Anatomy class in medical school. That cadaver was cool to the touch, leathery and gray-white. The cadaver appeared more like a dull, plastic anatomical model than a person. The body of Mr. Gray was different; he appeared only to be sleeping. Overall, he was a massive man with a bushy reddish beard and long hair. His arms lay at his sides with his palms facing upward and his hands were thick and roughened like those of a workman. But his most prominent feature was his enormous abdomen that towered above the table like a fleshy dome.

"Look at that ascites, man." Said the resident, in a tone similar to a car salesman slapping a fender with pride.

Mr. Gray's abdomen was distended because like Mr. Garcia, he also suffered from a failing liver. Mr. Gray's liver failure was far more advanced, resulting in liters of ascites. Ascites is the name of the abundant watery fluid that fills the space inside the abdomen (peritoneal cavity) when it cannot properly drain.

"Push on it, Wolfe. Go on." He said.

I gave the abdomen a gentle nudge, which produced an undulation that is referred to as a 'fluid wave'. This test served two purposes: 1) it's a common physical exam technique to check for excess fluid in the abdomen (which Mr. Gray did have) and 2) a person who isn't dead might react in response to the nudge. Thankfully, he did not move but his radiating warmth was evident through his hospital gown. The thought that I had tried to keep out finally crept into my mind: *Might he still be alive?*

The resident guided me through the examination, which started at the head and moved downward as I tested various neurological and physiological functions that helped determine brain death.

"Test the pupillary reflex", he said flatly.

This is something I had done hundreds of times before on patients during my first two years of medical school. Mr. Gray's eyes were already half open. The area of the eyeball typically referred to as "the whites of the eyes" (sclera, plural = sclerae), were a vibrant yellow color. This common sign of liver failure is known as scleral icterus and is the result of the buildup of a protein called bilirubin. The clarity of his eyes was disturbing. I expected the corneas of a dead man to be clouded, but his death was so recent that I could see every striation of his crystal blue iris. I swung the light beam onto his eye; there was no pupil constriction, a sign of death.

The resident then handed me a cotton swab. "Brush the eye…touch the cotton to the cornea."

This would be a most uncomfortable procedure in the living; irritation of the cornea with a cotton swab should cause a person to blink and the eye to water. As I brushed the cornea with the dry cotton, I squinted my own eyes sympathetically. Mr. Gray did not blink. These were simple but time-honored neurological tests to assess for sensation and function of cranial nerves. Despite these negative tests, I just couldn't seem to shake the idea that he might still be alive, somehow. This was the paranoia of inexperience. I needed more information.

For the final part of the exam I moved just to the right side of Mr. Gray's chest to listen to his heart and lungs. He was a large man even without his pathologically expanded abdomen. I leaned over his chest and hovered close to him as I placed the stethoscope's earpieces into my ears. I could feel the warmth[2] of his body on my flank as I pressed the bell of the stethoscope firmly onto his chest. I closed my eyes, held my breath and listened. A tiny *thump* sent a shock through me and I recoiled from Mr. Gray's body. The resident glared at me like a disappointed parent. It was my own fingers on the rubber edge of the bell that produced the errant noise. I listened again over multiple areas of the chest. There was no familiar *lub-dub* of the beating heart and no *whoosh* sounds of inhaled air coursing through the lungs. I confirmed that his chest was a chasm of inactivity and stepped away from the hospital bed. Mr. Gray was dead. I wrote the results of the death exam as part of his final chart note and returned to my work on living patients for the time being.

***

So what can we learn from the death exam of Mr. Gray? Even after the cardiac monitor reaches a flatline, diagnosing death in the immediate postmortem period of the freshly dead can be an unsettling task. Early in a zombiism outbreak, before the disease is well characterized, this will be a dangerous task if the zombie suddenly reanimates. The example of Mr. Gray's basic death exam is more about illustrating which features one may have to assess on a potential zombie. In the absence of overt consciousness, at minimum one will have to test for breathing and circulation. Simply feeling for a pulse or placing a spoon under the nostrils to look for fogging could be good enough in the non-

---

[2] Radiant heat from a corpse is quite common. In the freshly dead, the body temperature can stay the same or increase slightly for a time, due to the combined effects of heat generated by the metabolism of cell breakdown and unchecked bacterial growth.

hospital setting. One must exercise great caution since the time immediately after reanimation may be the most aggressive period for the zombie.

Although death determination is key for defining Type 1 from Type 2 zombies, this is a concern mostly in the infected and (apparently) dying or the freshly dead. In those individuals that exhibit active signs of decay, the diagnosis of Type 1 zombiism can quickly be made and the appropriate strategies implemented. The following section details the signs of decomposition that are observed and described by forensic pathologists at the time of autopsy.

Late Signs of Death: Decomposition

In the previous section we dealt with how to determine death in the freshly dead and corpses that do not yet show signs of decomposition. But what of someone who has died days, weeks or even months prior? There are signs based on the predictable sequence of decomposition of the human body. The type of death signs we examine here go well beyond the level of what was observed in Mr. Gray, as he did not show any signs of decomposition.

Decomposition of the human body is a function of autolysis, bacterial growth, environmental factors and time. **Autolysis** refers to the destruction of cells and tissues by their own enzymes. During life, the cells of our organs are nourished by oxygen and various nutrients that are delivered in the blood. Once the heart no longer pumps, the tissues and organs of the body can no longer receive the contents of the blood. This causes cellular metabolism to cease. Enzymes that are normally in check begin to degrade proteins, nucleic acids (DNA, RNA) and sugars. As the process continues, our own enzymes begin to destroy the very cells they were there to protect and maintain. The process of autolysis varies depending on the organ in which it occurs. Dense organs like the liver and kidneys maintain their shape but very soft organs like the brain and spleen begin to liquefy into a soup of protein and cellular debris.

While the process of autolysis begins the body's breakdown, there is a part of us that is still very much alive after our consciousness fades away: bacteria. During life, bacteria coat the surface of the skin and the entire gastrointestinal tract from top to bottom. During life, these single-celled organisms harmlessly colonize the body and do not produce infection. After death, overgrowth of these bacteria produce the changes of decomposition that can be seen on surface examination of the body, and primarily involve bloating due to production of gases and the production of other compounds that change the color of the corpse.

An extremely important factor in decomposition is whether the body was located indoors or outdoors. A body shielded from the elements of extreme temperature, moisture and sunlight will decompose more slowly than a body that is outdoors. The following are features of the not so freshly dead: bodies that are past the immediate postmortem period and have begun to decay. Signs of decay are definitive evidence of a Type 1 (Resurrected Dead) zombie.

Skin Slippage & Bullae Formation

The outer layer of the skin (epidermis) is composed of cells called squamous cells. These cells produce keratin and are held together in a mesh-like fashion by microscopic protein bridges. The presence of keratin is why intact human skin is waterproof and reasonably resistant to minor injuries. But when the body dies, autolysis causes the protein junctions to break apart. On a corpse, this causes the outer layer of skin to slide off the body with even the lightest amount of friction or pressure.

When the skin begins to slip and break from the underlying deep skin layer (known as the dermis) sometimes the outer layer remains intact and watery fluid fills these areas, forming blisters known as "bullae" (pronounced "Bull-Ay"; singular 'bulla'). These tend to develop along with skin slippage because it is the same underlying process of skin protein breakdown. Zombies manifesting these changes begin to decay rapidly and tend to have a wet appearance because of all the weeping fluid from the broken blisters. Subsequent drying of these areas causes the decaying skin to darken, giving the corpse a green-gray to black appearance. Both skin slippage and bullae formation can occur in the first 24 hours or even faster if death occurs in a warm climate or if there is exposure to direct sunlight. At mild temperatures this may not occur for a few days.

Rigor Mortis

Translated from Latin, *rigor* means 'stiff' and *mortis*, means death. Immediately after death and for short period of time, the body lacks muscle tone and is flaccid like a rag doll. The muscles begin to stiffen a few hours after death due to cross-linking of proteins between muscle fibers. When a muscle flexes during life, the proteins slide back and forth next to each other by locking in and releasing. After death, the proteins lock but do not release and get increasingly tighter during the process of rigor mortis. This increases over the first one to two days then begins to release as muscle proteins break down due to autolysis. After a few days, rigor mortis is completely absent—the body is a bag of bones and decomposing flesh. Once it dissipates, rigor mortis never returns. For the purposes making a diagnosis on sight, there aren't many conditions in the living that can produce complete flaccidity or sustained muscular contraction. Either condition would produce death in short order regardless of the cause. It should be noted that rigor mortis can develop instantaneously after death if the person is engaged in extreme physical activity such as sprinting or the struggle that occurs during drowning. This is known as **cadaveric spasm**.

Livor Mortis

Livor mortis refers to the settling of blood after death due to the effect of gravity. The word livor is from a Latin word meaning bluish-purple. This refers to the bluish-purple discoloration of the skin in areas where the blood pools. When the heart stops beating the blood pressure goes to zero (0 systolic/0 diastolic) and the only force moving blood through the vessels is gravity. In forensics, the pattern of this drainage of blood can give an indication of the position of the body at the time of death. For example, if one dies lying on their back and the body is not moved, the blood will drain to the back of the head, trunk and backs of the arms and legs. If someone dies by hanging, the blood will pool in the legs, forearms and hands. This sign is not particularly useful in the diagnosis of zombiism, mainly because   clothing or late signs of decomposition may obstruct view of the skin.

Vascular Marbling

The appearance of vascular marbling is one of the most visually distinct signs of death. After we die—and assuming we do not die of excessive blood loss—the blood vessels that course through our bodies still contain liquid blood. Blood is a protein-rich, cellular substance and like flesh, also begins to decay. The red blood cells contain the oxygen-carrying protein called hemoglobin. The process of hemoglobin breakdown imparts a stain on the wall of the blood vessel and the surrounding tissues. This is known as **vascular marbling**. The term 'marbling' is used because of the way the vessels have an appearance on the skin similar to streaks coursing through marble. (See Figure 2.1). Marbling is a feature that is usually seen in the time frame of 3 to 5 days after death.

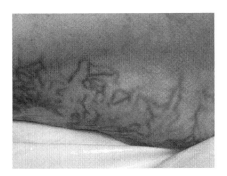

Figure 2.1.   Vascular Marbling. The blood vessel pattern in the skin gives an
appearance similar to that of marble. © DLWolfe.

Algor Mortis

The least famous of the 'mortis' family, algor mortis, is translated from Latin to mean "coolness of death". The body cools at about 2.0 degrees Fahrenheit per hour for the first few hours after death then the cooling rate slows to about 1.0 degree per hour until reaching ambient temperature. A body in a morgue refrigerator might cool all the way to 37° F (2.8° C). However, a person dying in a 117° F (47° C) desert would not cool but would instead warm to the surrounding environment.

Bloating and Discoloration

No matter how much antibacterial soap or hand gel we use, bacteria are everywhere on our bodies and in the environment. Most are harmless and can even be helpful to our physiologic wellbeing. But in death, these bacteria are the source of our decay from within the body, particularly the bacteria found in the gastrointestinal tract. In fact, the first sign of decomposition is often at the right lower abdomen because the cecum (the first part of the large intestine) is closest to the abdominal wall at this area. The continued action of bacterial growth can produce a green discoloration of the skin over the entire surface of the body. Eventually, the green color becomes so intense that the intact skin may appear charcoal black.

Bacteria are also why corpses bloat after death due to the production of gases such as methane (CH_3), hydrogen (H_2), and sulfur (S)-containing gases called mercaptans. Because of the high bacterial content in the intestines prior to death, the abdomen can become filled like a balloon. The distended abdomen becomes so hard from gaseous pressure that the passage of a scalpel during the opening incision of autopsy can cause a loud 'pop' and *whoosh* of foul-smelling gases that fill the morgue. In addition, the face may swell and the tongue may protrude from the mouth due to gas-filled tissues within the throat and oral cavity. Eventually, tiny gas pockets form in all soft tissues of the body which then become "crepitant to palpation", which means having a consistency like bubble wrap. In men, the scrotum and penis can massively swell because gases can seep into these areas due to the close proximity to the abdomen.

Insect Activity (Maggots)

The presence of maggots on or inside the body is evidence that this is a truly a Type 1 zombie. Maggots, which are the larvae of common flies, feed only on necrotic (dead) tissue. One must use judgment, however, because dead tissue can occur in someone who is living. This is typically found around an existing wound or ulcer. This is likely why ancient physicians used maggots to treat open wounds. Maggots are so efficient at clearing away dead tissue, that in 2004 the Food and Drug Administration (FDA) approved their use in debridement of ulcers and other non-healing wounds in humans. An earlier diagnostic clue of death is the presence of fly eggs. The earliest stage of fly eggs look like sawdust and tend to aggregate in moist areas, such as around the corners of the eyes, the mouth or any open wounds or injuries. If you suspect a creature could be a zombie and you see what looks like sawdust on the skin, be on guard. These are most likely fly eggs and will rapidly develop into maggots of increasing size over a short period of time. The rate and scope of maggot development is highly dependent on temperature. A zombie in Saskatchewan, Canada in December would not develop maggots as quickly as a zombie in Tampa, Florida in July.

Odor of Decomposition (The 'Smell of Death")

The smell of death in context with other features of decomposition would be diagnostic of the Resurrected Dead. So what is the smell of death really like? A freshly dead body has no particular odor at all until the abdominal cavity is opened. Even then, the bowel does not have a particularly bad odor until there is advanced bacterial growth in the colon or an abscess in the abdomen. But this differs from the odor of decomposition. The stench of decomposing flesh has been described as sickly sweet, pungent and slightly acrid (irritating). It is a smell that can be provocative of the senses and the uninitiated can become nauseous and need to urgently leave the morgue. Seasoned death investigators and autopsy specialists build up a tolerance to this odor and can largely ignore it during the examination of the dead body. The only way to really understand the smell of death is to experience it once.

Mummification

Mummification is a kind of decomposition well beyond the usual of timeline of the above changes. Instead of days, mummification occurs over weeks and months. It is worth noting that this does not refer to the mummification process described in ancient Egypt or in the Incan tribes of South America. Non-ritual mummification is observed in bodies that were undiscovered for weeks or months after having died indoors. Instead of breaking down, bodies undergoing mummification remain intact. The skin appears dry, dark and firm, almost like a piece of leather. Subcutaneous fat wastes away, giving a sunken appearance to the eyes and soft tissue of the face. The hair becomes brittle and the fingernails and toenails appear longer due to retraction of the skin and cuticle. This is the origin of the myth that hair and nails grow after death. They don't.

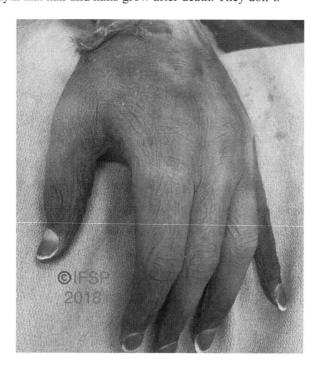

Figure 2.2. Mummification. Note the dried, darkened appearance of the hands and fingernails. © IFSP.

The diagnosis of death seems like a no-brainer. But as was demonstrated by the case of Mr. Gray, it is more involved than just giving someone a nudge and seeing if they move. In the clinical setting, the confirmation of death has been redefined over the years as technology to assess brain function continues to develop. Certainly, in the early part of a zombie outbreak (prior to the apocalypse), wards will be filled with patients who exhibit signs of death but may need precise confirmation to determine the next steps. Death will be the key determinant for treatment plans, quarantine strategies and neutralization strategies ("killing" the zombie for lack of a better term), which is described in Part III of this book.

Brief History of Zombiology Origins

The notion of zombiism, commonly understood as a form of malignant resurrection, is rooted in myths, religious traditions and the genuine uncertainty of some early cultures that the dead *might not* stay dead. In ancient Greece, graves have been unearthed in which corpses were pinned down with heavy rocks or restrained in other ways, to protect the living. More recently, the 19th and early 20th century accounts of "voodoo zombies" described in West Africa and Caribbean islands have been a direct inspiration for modern zombie fiction.

The legend of the voodoo zombie is thought to have begun when a priest known as a "bokor" prepared special powders or solutions made from plants and animals native to the local environment. These concoctions likely contained tetrodotoxin, a type of neurotoxin (a chemical that acts on brain and/or nerves) found within the puffer fish and other marine creatures. A person who ingested such an elixir attained such profound unconsciousness that they appeared to have died and were prematurely prepared for a funeral ceremony. As the toxin wore off, the person would rise without warning and would have difficulty speaking (dysarthria) and with walking and coordination (ataxia). The appearance of a seemingly freshly dead corpse that is moaning and staggering along is close to the modern conception of the risen dead, Type 1 zombie.

Adding to zombie hysteria, there are real examples every year in the news where a person is suspected to be dead, only to be rescued when found knocking on the morgue cooler from the inside. These cases occur almost exclusively in countries that have a poorly defined death investigation system and result from some patients being bagged and sent to the morgue while in a coma state. The examples of resurrection in religious traditions are well established. In particular, the central figure in Christianity is said to have risen from the dead. However, it should be noted that this was not a zombie as we currently define it, because there was no subsequent attacking, cannibalism or infectious disease. This rare subtype of "Benevolent Zombie" will not be covered in this book.

***

Modern zombiology has come a long way since the days of graveyard resurrections and the easily defeated rotting corpses. Instead of death being the starting point for diagnosis it has instead become a fulcrum point between the Type 1 (dead) and Type 2 (living) zombies. As contemporary science and medicine take a foothold in the field, more is understood about how zombies can be diagnosed and classified. Zombiism is no longer confined to the realm of a nebulous supernatural cause but we can now describe the zombie disease in terms of actual biological or chemical/drug agents. By doing so, we set the stage for a deeper understanding of the affliction and ultimately how to best deal with it.

Part II:

Etiology: The Proposed Causes of Zombiism

There was a time when the cause for zombiism was an open and shut case. It's simply a virus, right? If only zombiology was that simple. There is an array of potential zombiism causes from the worlds of microbiology and biochemistry that could be responsible for the disease. Whether the cause is viral, bacterial or chemical, a zombiism agent must produce the typical symptoms of zombiism in a reproducible fashion. Although we focus heavily on microbiological causes in this chapter, the template for how Type 2 zombiism will look symptomatically has already been provided for us in the real world: the cases of profound aggression and attacking behavior caused by certain street drugs.

Excited Delirium and the Blueprint for Zombiism

The worlds of chemistry and pharmacology provide perhaps the most intriguing explanation for zombiism, since many chemicals and drugs act on very specific targets within the body. The specificity of a biochemical or cellular target is the key to reproducible and persistent zombiism symptoms. Cases of drug-based zombie behavior actually best demonstrate for us which brain structures might be affected to produce Type 2 zombiism, infectious or otherwise.

Coursing through our blood and bathing the space between every one of our 100 billion brain cells is a mixture of proteins, sugars, hormones and other biological chemicals. An imbalance in the production or removal of these neurochemicals can cause behavioral or neurological symptoms. There are an untold number of chemical compounds that can act on the brain to produce feelings of euphoria, depression, anger, and every imaginable emotion. As such, humans are constantly experimenting with molecules that can improve mood, and there is some overlap between what is produced at a pharmaceutical company and what might be produced and used illegally on the street. Is there a drug compound that can produce 'chemical zombiism'? Some real world examples suggest this may be possible.

In Miami, FL in 2012, an attack occurred that was so unusual that it was reported in national and worldwide news. A completely naked man with extreme aggression attacked and devoured the face and eyes of a homeless person in broad daylight. Upon arrival of officers, the attack was still in progress and they shouted for the man to stop. He looked up, growled at them and then returned to eating the man's face. An officer opened fire, hitting the attacker once, but this did not stop him. The aggressor took four more bullets into his body before he was neutralized.

Initially, it was believed the man had taken in 'bath salts' to produce this extreme aggression reaction. This display of attacking behavior and 'superhuman' strength is what is known as **excited delirium**. Excited delirium has been described since the 1800s and was classically associated with cocaine use. In recent times, it's been associated more often with methamphetamine, PCP (phencyclidine) and newer drugs under the names "flakka", "bath salts" and "Spice/K2". Any drug that can produce excited delirium is a prime candidate for Type 2, chemical zombiism.

The media branded the incident the "Miami Bath Salts Zombie' and it became a top headline. Zombies always seem to get views and ad clicks (and sell books?) and people ran with it. Was this man really a zombie? Were there more out there? The incident got so much fanfare that the Centers for Disease Control (CDC) actually released the following statement:

"CDC does not know of a virus or condition that would reanimate the dead (or one that would present zombie-like symptoms)."[3]

There was also much confusion as to what 'bath salts' even meant. Many people out there thought that smoking the bath salts in their grandmother's medicine cabinet would produce some kind of intense high. This was completely false. The drugs known as "bath salts" are from a class of chemicals called synthetic cathinones. These are man-made versions of cathinone, a chemical found in an East African/Middle Eastern plant called Khat. Cathinone is used as a stimulant and is similar to methamphetamine and cocaine in its effects on human physiology. The synthetic versions of these drugs are extremely addictive and are well known to produce an extreme excited delirium.

The twist in this story is that the toxicology samples obtained during autopsy of the Bath Salts "Zombie" were negative for 'bath salts'/cathinone chemicals. The only substance in the blood was reported to be cannabis/marijuana (THC). Marijuana can cause the user to eat more, but typically this does not include human faces. Despite the negative results, the autopsy revealed that there were numerous undigested white pills in his stomach. The

---

[3] We bristle at the CDC's continued outdated suggestions that a zombie only be a Type 1 (Resurrected Dead) or that a virus is the causative agent.

pills were not identifiable as any type of known medication. It is reasonable to assume that the substance in those pills likely produced the zombiism symptoms. So if he clearly took pills that contained a drug then how could the toxicology test be negative? In short, a test can only be positive for a substance if it is one that can be tested for. It is possible that someone could ingest a new formulation of a street drug that toxicologists and chemists simply haven't even seen yet. This is the case with many of the street drugs that are chemically altered. These changes often involve subtle molecular variations that allow the drug to evade detection.

Some have theorized that such aggressive behavior with negative blood toxicology could also represent a psychotic episode. This is not an unreasonable explanation but almost all of these excited delirium incidents involve some kind of witnessed ingestion prior to the attacking behavior. So how could a drug or chemical result in reproducible and persistent symptoms of zombiism? While this may seem far-fetched, there are examples of drugs that selectively destroy functional areas of the brain.

In 1976, a chemistry graduate student attempted to synthesize MPPP, an opioid drug similar to morphine and meperidine (Demerol) and injected the resulting substance. Within a couple of days he began to develop severe tremors and eventually developed full Parkinson's Disease, a type of degenerative movement disorder. Outside of genetic forms of the disease, Parkinson's does not develop until much later in life, but the graduate student was in his 20's. He never recovered. A few years later in Santa Clara County, California, four individuals were diagnosed with severe Parkinson's symptoms after using the MPPP drug. As it turned out, in both the graduate student and the Santa Clara cases, an impurity was present. This chemical impurity was identified as MPTP and can have a devastating effect on areas of the brain that specifically control movement. Individuals that died after taking the drug were autopsied, and it was revealed that the neurons of the substantia nigra were obliterated. The substantia nigra literally means 'black substance' due to its dark appearance in the brain tissue and is the area in the brain known to produce dopamine. Without dopamine production, a patient will develop Parkinson's Disease.

The cases are instructive in that it shows that a specific chemical compound can selectively destroy highly specialized areas of the brain tissue. If a drug or toxin was developed that could affect the areas that are responsible for extreme aggression, this would undoubtedly be a strong candidate for Chemical or Drug-Induced Zombiism. The drugs that typically produce excited delirium, such as synthetic cathinones (Bath Salts), synthetic cannabinoids (K2/Spice) and methamphetamine, all have synthetic processes which can result in impurities. A bad batch of a drug could produce a limited outbreak of zombiism. The bigger concern would be an introduction of such chemicals into a large reservoir (like a water supply) that could produce an epidemic of profoundly aggressive, chemical-induced zombies. This could be intentional (chemical warfare) or accidental (industrial accident). Such an epidemic could cause local chaos but would not rise to the level of apocalyptic zombiism unless the agent affected an enormous geographic area or large swath of the population.

Architecture of Aggression

The exact neurobiology of aggression, impulse control and violence is beyond the scope of this book. However, the known actions of drugs that cause these symptoms could provide a road map to how a causative agent could trigger zombiism. Even if the zombie agent (infectious or chemical) could be transmitted easily and get inside the body to do its damage, how exactly would it cause the symptoms? The typical conception of the brain is a soft gray blob of mush with a wrinkly surface. But within that blob there are areas that govern highly specific functions. From our ability to move, taste sweetness, feel love, see colors and even breathe, the blueprint for existence is present in these groups of neurons. As such, there are specific areas within the brain that control personality, impulses and aggression. For the zombie agent to cause what we know as zombiism, it would need to produce a "pathologic effect" in these areas of the brain. This could be destruction of areas that inhibit aggression and violence, or persistent activation of those areas that cause aggression.

The brain has a system of checks and balances to prevent such persistent activations and overreactions. Areas of the brain governing emotion and "fight or flight" response are considered *old* from an evolutionary perspective. One such area is the amygdala, and is central to the primal "fear response" in animals and humans. The prefrontal cortex of the brain (a part near the front of the brain) helps us control aggressive tendencies and negative thoughts. In other words, as the amygdala heats up and makes us feel aggressive, the prefrontal cortex helps pour cold water on those thoughts and actions. Studies performed on violent criminals (murderers and death row inmates) have shown a decreased activity of the prefrontal cortex, suggesting that the aggression arising from the amygdala is unable to be stopped by the usual control mechanism.

There are also hormonal and biochemical factors that play a role in aggression. Testosterone can increase aggression in both men and women, whereas the neurochemical serotonin can act to diminish aggressive tendencies. In the cases of excited delirium, the most important neurochemical is dopamine. Dopamine has many functions and is a chemical released when we experience pleasurable activities and can also aid in choosing to avoid negative activities. Too much of it, however, can produce paranoia, mania and extreme aggression, the symptoms of Type 2 zombiism. This is what happens when some individuals take cocaine, synthetic marijuana (K2/Spice), phencyclidine (PCP) or synthetic cathinones. Except instead of a drug activating these areas, it would be the infectious agent itself.

Infectious Zombiism: The Candidates

Viruses: Submicroscopic Machines of Death and Disease

Most of the general public expects that it is a virus that will be the cause of an eventual zombie apocalypse. Certainly, viruses for which we have no natural immunity can produce overwhelming amounts of death, as was evidenced by the 1918 Spanish flu, which is estimated to have killed more than 50 million people worldwide in just one year. In modern times, with the ease of worldwide travel and increasingly dense areas of population, it is reasonable to imagine that an apocalyptic virus could manifest. As was also shown with the mini-outbreaks of SARS (2003) and H7N9 Bird flu (1997), a virus can spread quickly and kill efficiently. But is there a reasonable biological basis for the virus as the cause of zombiism? First we must understand some basics about viral biology to understand how they could cause Type 2 infectious zombiism.

Viruses are ancient biological forms and existed before us and will exist long after our kind has faded from the surface of the planet. These unusual organisms can affect the body in a variety of ways and in just about every known human tissue. Viruses exist in a kind of biological inertia because they cannot grow outside of their human host. A virus is kind a submicroscopic "machine" composed of nucleic acids (RNA or DNA) inside an envelope made of proteins or lipids. To survive and reproduce, the virus must get inside of a *living* host and attach to a cell surface. Once inside the cell, the viral machine turns on and uses the host cells' enzymes and raw materials to replicate itself. Replication continues until the cell bursts, spilling thousands of new viruses onto nearby cells and starting the process all over again. The irony of the virus is that in order to live, it must kill cells in the host. If a viral infection is too severe, the living host may die, thus ending the life cycle of the virus.

So why has the virus become such a popular plot device in zombie fiction? Maybe it's because "virus" is a nice generic term for any 'cause of a disease that doesn't need to be further explained.' We've all went to the doctor and been told it's "probably a virus"; although that may be true, it can be translated as "I'm not sure exactly what's causing your symptoms but it's probably not bad enough to kill you." Except in the case of zombiism, the virus will absolutely kill you.

There are thousands of types of viruses that affect humans and animals, but only a subset of these infect the brain. Some are self-limited and may only cause fever, headache and fatigue while others may cause severe symptoms and death. On occasion, the worst effects of the virus may occur after the infection has long past. These post-viral infection syndromes are thought to be due to the action of our own immune system against the brain or spinal cord tissue. The following viral profiles are what we deem the most likely to produce zombiism or zombie-like symptoms based on how these viruses are known to behave in humans.

Zombie Virus Candidate 1: The Rabies Virus

It's a curious thing that virtually all zombies seem to transmit the infection with a bite. Naturally, the rabies virus (or something like it) has become one of the most popular theoretical causes for infectious zombiism. In its natural state, the rabies virus is a **zoonosis**, a disease transmitted to humans via an infected animal. Rabies infections are typically associated with animals such as bats, raccoons, skunks and foxes but can also be found in domestic animals such as dogs and cats.

When an infected animal bites, its sharp, saliva-coated teeth puncture deeply into the underlying flesh, carrying the deadly virus with it. Once in the wound, the virus attaches to nerves and begins its long journey to the brain where it exerts its devastating effects. At the beginning of the illness, the patient may complain of nonspecific symptoms like fatigue, headache and fever. As the viral incubation continues, even subtle movements of the body or pressure on the skin can produce extreme pain (allodynia) and marked sensitivity to light (photophobia). In the final stage, rabies patients have severe psychological changes such as extreme agitation and mania. The classic 'foaming at the mouth' sign occurs due to an aversion to swallowing one's own saliva, which causes it to collect around the mouth. All rabies cases end with death.

There are obstacles to the actual rabies virus causing zombiism. Rabies is difficult to get and even more difficult to spread because it generally requires a bite. Because animal to human bite transmission is uncommon, the disease is uncommon in the developed world. But it is this combination of biting with neurological and psychiatric symptoms that make it one of the most popular candidates for zombiism. So how could it make the leap from affecting a handful of humans per year to one of an apocalyptic threat? In short, virus mutation.

Mutation is the process by which organisms can change in order to bring about a new feature. This occurs in all living organisms and may result in advantages or disadvantages and is the basis for natural selection and evolution. For the rabies virus, the zombiism threat would become more tangible if the virus mutates to become more communicable from animals to humans and of course from humans to other humans. Secondly, rabies can take many weeks or months to manifest after the initial infection. This is far too long of a time period to trigger an outbreak; apocalyptic type infections need to spread fast and easily. This is why we feel that the mutated rabies virus must have these qualities and we refer to this as a "rabies-*like* virus" (RLV).

But how would an outbreak of RLV play out? Although we would expect the disease to move more swiftly through the population compared with rabies, there would probably be a delay in diagnosis. Such a delay would prevent health care professionals from knowing how to treat it and health departments might not effectively quarantine those who are exposed to the disease. Diagnosis is paramount, but making the diagnosis would not be as easy as drawing a blood sample. In the case of rabies, the diagnosis can only be confirmed at autopsy. This presumably would be the same for RLV. Once the patient (or animal) dies, the pathologist examines brain samples in the microscope and the characteristic changes are observed. The problem is, this takes time.

Whereas influenza can now be diagnosed in the clinic in under an hour, the process of RLV diagnosis might take weeks, especially early in the outbreak. This would be critical time lost between the start of the outbreak and the discovery of the agent. This also has implications for treatment and vaccination. The current rabies virus has a vaccine that is 100% effective and a rabies-specific antibody can be given to the patient to neutralize the virus before it makes its way to the brain. Therefore, an RLV infection might be able to be halted with a vaccine, but this would likely take several months to develop once the virus is discovered and isolated. Depending on the rate that the disease spreads and the numbers of people killed, it could be too late.

Zombie Virus Candidate 2: Measles Virus

Over the last few decades, medical students were taught about measles infections mostly for historical insight and to prepare students who might eventually practice in an undeveloped country where measles is still a problem. Measles has recently returned in limited epidemics in many areas of the developed world. Clinically, the most common picture of the measles patient is a feverish child with a bright red spotted skin rash. The infection usually resolves after days of the child feeling miserable, but a portion of patients can develop a very serious neurological complication called Subacute Sclerosing Panencephalitis (SSPE). The key term to remember is "panencephalitis", which means 'inflammation affecting all areas of the brain'. SSPE results from a measles virus with many genetic changes and can occur months to years after an initial measles infection. The symptoms include decline of reasoning and ability to think, seizures, or spasticity of the arms and the legs.

Given that neurological, muscular and psychiatric changes can occur with SSPE, it is an interesting template for an unusual form of viral zombiism. In the case of SSPE, it is not communicable, but the complication is an instructive example of how the virus can alter function of the brain long after the usual symptoms of measles have passed. To rise to the level of an apocalyptic effect, an altered measles virus that can produce a syndrome like SSPE but affect a higher proportion of the population. Such an epidemic would most likely be limited to a few geographic locations or certain groups of people. The bigger picture of the measles/SSPE sequence is that viruses can on occasion produce complications that affect the patient for years and sometimes for the rest of their lives. If a condition like SSPE involved areas of the brain responsible for aggression and attacking behaviors, it could be an unusual form of non-communicable zombiism. Such a disease would likely not have any effective treatment.

<u>Zombie Virus Candidate 3: Arthropod-borne Viruses (Arbovirus)</u>

There are many viruses that are spread by arthropod vectors. An **arthropod** is an invertebrate animal and includes insects, spiders and even crustaceans. Viruses carried and transmitted by arthropods are called **arboviruses**. Many of these viruses affect the central nervous system and cause **encephalitis**, an inflammation/infection of the brain tissue itself. For the purposes of zombiism, we focus mainly on mosquitos, which are vectors for dozens of human diseases. Some viruses commonly transmitted by mosquitos include dengue fever, West Nile Virus, Eastern and Western Equine Encephalitis and Japanese encephalitis to name a few. Because so many of the arboviruses preferentially infect brain tissue, we must give the group consideration as a potential agent of zombiism. Most individuals with viral encephalitis recover without any complications, while others may have fatigue or psychiatric changes. Rarely, death may occur. Arboviruses are also compelling because so many of the "new" or emerging infectious diseases seem to come from arthropods. Mosquito-borne diseases in particular have been in the news frequently over the last several years, including the Zika virus that was shown to cause severe brain defects in fetuses. A less common virus, chikungunya, causes fever and joint pain but some patients go on to develop encephalitis and neurological symptoms.[4]

At current, the arboviruses that can cause encephalitis do not typically rise to the level of aggression, delirium or mania. But the potential for a dangerous outbreak exists because of the wide range of diseases carried by arthropod vectors and the coexistence of humans and mosquitoes in the same geographic areas. If an arthropod-borne virus were to arise that preferentially infects and destroys areas of the brain that results in unchecked aggression, this could cause limited outbreaks of zombiism. It is not likely that the disease could be passed person to person, and this diminishes the potential apocalyptic effect of the arbovirus.

The Prion:

Zombie Agent Neither Living Nor Dead

In the Gross Anatomy class during my first year of medical school, we were tasked with dissecting every centimeter of a male cadaver that we named Maxwell. Most of these dissections involved the tedious removal of tiny bits of soft tissue to uncover some small nerve or blood vessel branch. Many hours of tedious work would occasionally be punctuated by a major procedure that moved the dissection more quickly toward completion. One such procedure was harvesting Maxwell's brain for use in a Neuroanatomy course later in the year.

As a team, Adam, Johanna and myself had removed the skin from the scalp to prepare to open the skull with the bone saw. My ears rang from the harsh high-pitched saw motor as

---

[4] It should be noted that although these viruses are 'new' to the general public, both Zika and chikungunya were discovered in Africa 60 to 70 years ago

the blade ground through the dense skull bone. As Adam began working the saw through the skull to complete his cuts, my enthusiasm was quashed and I slowly moved back from the dissection table. There were clouds of brain and bone dust being ejected around Maxwell's head and pouring onto the dissection table. Adam and Johanna noticed my obvious aversion and stopped the saw.

They stood still, staring at me through their protective goggles. The words were spoken through their silent glare. *"What?!"*

I took a step toward the table, my eyes fixed on Maxwell's partially opened head.

"So…there's an awful lot of bone dust… coming from the skull. And some brain matter…Coming out of his head…into the air."

"So?" they seemed to say in unison.

"Well, I mean…what if this guy had a *prion disease*?"

They laughed. "A prion?" Johanna said. "You're such a jackass."[5]

"I'm serious! We don't know anything about this guy! If he had a prion disease we are all actively inhaling infected bone dust. Even formaldehyde won't inactivate prions. We're basically going to die a horrible degenerative death", I said.

Our instructor reassured us that the cadaver "probably" did not have a prion disease, and that we would all remain neurologically intact for now. We finished opening the head, removed the brain and went on with our usual dissections. Yet, I remained unsettled.

So what is a prion and why was I so worried about it? And how does it relate to zombiism? Like viruses, the story began a long time ago.

---

[5] This was a common phrase said to me during my first two years of medical school.

Spain, 1732

A sheepherder named Cyr noticed a strange disease had been affecting some of his sheep. The symptoms were so unusual that he felt compelled to write down what he saw:

(Translated): *"The sheep stumbled as they walked, often falling over. When they tried to get to their feet they wobbled unsteadily. They smacked their mouths and constantly stuck out their tongues and licked. Most unusual was how they drooped their heads and rubbed them on the ground, on rocks and on tree trunks and fence posts. Their fur was worn down to the flesh, and even the flesh was worn away in some areas down to the bone. For days, this went on and nothing could get them to stop. They refused food and water. Eventually they stopped moving altogether and died shortly after."*

Other herders noticed a similar disease in their flocks and goats were also being affected. None of them could stop *scraping* their heads on hard surfaces. Eventually the disease gained a name based on this behavior: Scrapie. For more than 200 years, the underlying cause of scrapie remained unknown. The mystery deepened elsewhere in the world.

Papua New Guinea, 1957

Under orders of the Australian government, scientists landed on the island nation of Papua New Guinea to study an unusual and devastating disease epidemic among the local peoples known as the Fore (pronounced For-ay) tribe. Doctors who had previously visited the island noted some very disturbing symptoms in the tribe, including uncontrolled shaking of the body and bouts of unintentional laughter. The disease was called *kuru*, which is from the Fore word meaning, "to shake". The cause was a mystery but the locals believed that ghosts or an evil witchcraft were responsible for the symptoms.

Doctors hoped for a more scientific explanation. The scientists that visited the island studied the cultural practices of the Fore for clues to the disease, which seemed to occur almost exclusively in women and children. It was found that the tribe had an unusual funeral practice that was at the root of what was causing *kuru*. When a tribe member died, the Fore engaged in ritual **endocannibalism**, which means the eating of one's own group or tribe. This is in contrast to **exocannibalism**, which is the eating of outsiders, commonly after defeating a tribe in battle or eating for survival. This type of ceremonial cannibalism was undertaken because the Fore believed that eating their dead could impart upon them wisdom or some special knowledge from their lost tribe member.

But the story of *kuru* gets even stranger. When a tribe member died, they would bury the corpse and wait a few days. Once maggots and other larvae developed, the corpse was exhumed, dismembered and then eaten by the tribe and the maggots were served as a side dish. For the ceremonial meal, the women and the children were served the brain and spinal cord, since these were considered to be the least nutritious body parts. It was designated that the men could eat the best cuts of meat, which were the muscles and other tissues of the body. As it turned out, only the women and children developed *kuru,* because it was the brain and spinal cord that contained the deadly infectious agent.

Symptoms of kuru would start several years after ingesting the infected brains. It started with difficulty walking, loss of coordination, and difficulty speaking. Eventually the afflicted stopped talking and would lay in one place, virtually unable to move. Then the laughing would begin. Inappropriate or uncontrolled fits of laughing are a symptom of the disease that caused it to earn the unofficial moniker of Laughing Sickness. Tissue samples were taken from those with *kuru* and after years of research the cause was finally identified and a new age had dawned in infectious disease.

This biological agent wasn't even a living organism; it was what is now known as a *prion*. The word **prion** (pree-on) was coined in 1982 and is a combination of the words '**pr**otein' and "infec**tion**'. The prion has a normal form that is designated as PrP. PrP is harmless, but when it is converted to the deadly abnormal form, it is written as PrP^{sc}, with "sc" standing for 'scrapie'. This notation has been used to denote the abnormal form of the prion even when the disease is not actually scrapie.

kuru was the first disease in which the infectious prion was definitively identified in the patients who had the disease. This was a quiet landmark moment in the history of human epidemiology and infectious disease, but prions would finally be introduced to the world stage with the first prion disease that would become a household name: Mad Cow Disease.

England 1986 - 1996

In the mid-1980s, the cattle farmers of the United Kingdom began noticing something disturbing in their herds. Some cows were struggling to get to their feet. Their weak legs wobbled and the animal made low guttural sounds. Over time, the cows grew thin and were unable to lift themselves to walk. It didn't take long for farmers and scientists alike to recognize that this was significant and terrifying; it looked like a cattle version of scrapie. This was extremely concerning because these cattle were being raised for the purpose of food. Veterinary pathologists were concerned that the condition was the devastating prion-based disease known as bovine spongiform encephalopathy (BSE), more commonly known across the world as "Mad Cow Disease".

If cattle had developed the prion disease and humans then consumed those cattle, then the public would be at risk for also developing a prion disease. It quickly became clear that the problem was much bigger than expected. Mad Cow continued to increase in incidence and by January 1993, there were more than 1,000 new cases of Mad Cow Disease being diagnosed *each week*.

As brain scientists and veterinary experts began to investigate the disease, they had to perform necropsies of the animals. A **necropsy** is another word for autopsy, but this term is more commonly used when doing a postmortem exam on an animal. The examination of the brain tissue under the microscope revealed the diagnosis: the neurons in the gray matter of the brain had a "Swiss cheese" like appearance. These 'holes' give rise to the term 'spongiform', referring to the key diagnostic feature of the cells having an appearance like a sponge. Additional testing was performed to confirm their suspicions of an abnormal prion protein.

Another entity had been added to the growing list of brain-degenerating prion diseases. There was concern that they would not know the extent of the disease for years because of the characteristic long incubation times of prions. This long incubation time meant that the cows diagnosed in 1986 must have contracted the prion years earlier. This also meant there could be other cows with the prion that had not yet shown symptoms.

Efforts were made to uncover the source of the disease and it is believed that Mad Cow arose as a result of cows being fed meat-and-bone meal (MBM), a cow-feed that contained the remains of other cows. It was suspected that the MBM feed must have been contaminated with the Mad Cow/BSE prion. The question was, if humans consumed the prion-tainted beef, then would they develop a human version of Mad Cow Disease? The answer to that question came just a few years later.

In the mid-1990s, several young people in England began to show extremely concerning symptoms. It started as simple forgetfulness or depression in teenagers and those in their twenties. Initially there was not much concern due to the high incidence of depression in the young adult age group. But then the hallucinations started. Shortly thereafter, the patients had difficulty walking. Then they became incontinent. The psychiatric symptoms got worse and the body wasted away. Eventually, the patients became bedridden and died about 1-2 years after symptoms started.

This disease had all the hallmarks of the prion diseases that had been previously described. At the time of the outbreak, there was confusion about cows actually being the source of the prion because at least two of the afflicted were vegetarians. However, it was believed that despite their current dietary habits, consumption of prion-infected beef products during their childhood was to blame. This fit with the long incubation period of prion-based diseases. Testing of the brain tissue after the death of these human patients revealed the presence of a disease that looked like Mad Cow, and it became known as vCJD, or 'variant Creutzfeldt Jakob Disease'[6].

In the end, such feared and incurable diseases resulted in swift action by the government and public health systems in both Britain and Australia. When authorities suspected that

---

[6] In 1920, the usual type of Creutzfeldt Jakob Disease (CJD) was named after two German pathologists that described a condition in elderly patients with symptoms like a fast-developing Alzheimer's Disease. Although Drs. Creutzfeld and Jakob did not know it at the time, the disease they described was the first human prion disease.

cannibalism may be the cause of *kuru*, the practice was banned under authority of the Australian government. When it was found that some cows were carrying a deadly prion, the British government decided to cull the herds, killing 2 million cattle. There have been few vCJD cases diagnosed since then and these may have been related to the initial exposure in the 1980s and 1990s. Both the *kuru* disease and vCJD have now been virtually eradicated.

So how do these unusual infectious proteins relate to zombiism? In short, what agent could be more terrifying than one with no vaccine, no treatment and no way to know you have it until the symptoms have started? Prion diseases are thankfully uncommon but what if they were spread more easily and did damage to the brain much more rapidly? This is the basis for the prion as the "Goldilocks" agent of zombiism; the potential perfect storm of a biologically 'invincible' agent that would devastate the population.

The Prion as the Goldilocks Agent of Zombiism

For an infectious disease to elevate to the level of a global threat, it must meet criteria that are *just right*. Just as the children's fairy tale character Goldilocks found the porridge, the chair and the bed that were 'just right', the infectious agent must be somewhere in the middle on key disease factors. If the disease spreads easily but has too short an incubation time, it may burn out locally before it spreads. If the disease is difficult to spread or has a long incubation time, it isn't likely affect large swathes of the population. If a disease kills too quickly, anyone who catches it will die before being able to infect others. But a Goldilocks agent will fit just right into these factors, producing maximal effect on the population, in the same way that previous pandemic diseases have been able to cause mass sickness and death in their own time.

The Goldilocks principle can be a useful thought experiment on how zombiism could bring about the much-feared zombie apocalypse. There are two main realms that would most likely allow for the Goldilocks Zombie: 1) a new naturally occurring disease 2) an engineered chemical agent or biological weapon. After an extensive review of both real and theoretical agents, our group proposes a cause for the coming zombie apocalypse: The Rapidly Infective Prion (RIP).

We know that prion diseases are fairly difficult to get, so how could it rise to the level of a worldwide zombiism threat? It seems that there is a need to ingest the prion agent to contract the disease. This means either eating something contaminated with the prion (contaminated beef, contaminated brains, etc.) or having something like prion-contaminated growth hormone treatments in which the infected substance is put directly into the body as a result of medical treatment. The latter is known as **iatrogenic** transmission. Thus, for a prion to make the jump from 'very rare' to 'apocalyptic' there would have to be some major changes in the ways the prion behaves in humans. Once again we return to the concept of molecular mutation.

Transmission of the Rapidly Infective Prion (RIP), PrP^Z

The nightmare scenario for humans is a deadly prion agent that is easily transmitted and fast acting within the body. This is the basis for the Rapidly Infective Prion (RIP), which can be denoted as PrP^Z. In pop culture depictions, infectious zombiism is typically transmitted by a bite. This is not ideal for a pandemic disease agent because infection is easily avoidable by simply taking shelter. It also limits who can transmit the disease: the elderly, babies and any patient without teeth would be unable to make an effective bite to spread the affliction. But prions might be transmitted in other ways.

There is evidence that scrapie prions may be shed in urine or feces and picked up by animals sharing the same space. Perhaps even more concerning, at least one study in mice revealed prions that were transmitted by aerosols (another word for droplet particles suspended in air). This is a worrisome finding, considering that mouse biology is so similar to humans that they are used for clinical drug trials. Studies in humans have shown that prions exist in virtually every fluid or tissue and this has resulted in some uncertainty about how transmission can occur. After the Mad Cow/vCJD scare, the concern was so great that US citizens were banned from donating blood if they had spent more than 3 months in the UK since 1980 or had ever had a blood transfusion there. This ban was despite no evidence that the prion was transmitted by blood transfusion. Such prion-infused blood and tissues would be a problem for transmission in the same way that viruses like hepatitis B or C or HIV are transmitted. And as it pertains to zombie "killing", getting sprayed with prion-infected blood or tissue would not be ideal; a concept discussed in Part III of the book.

Undoubtedly, the greatest impact for zombiism is if the prion could become much more easily transmissible, in particular if it could 'go airborne' like a typical respiratory virus. **Airborne transmission** refers to diseases that are spread by infectious organisms in 'droplet nuclei' expelled by the sick patient. When a patient coughs or sneezes, these infected droplets of oral or respiratory secretions can then hang in the air or move with air currents. As the droplets dehydrate (lose water), an invisible microscopic particle remains that contains the infectious agent. Anyone already in the room can then inhale these particles unknowingly and the infection can begin again in a new host. Examples of airborne diseases include tuberculosis (TB), SARS, measles, influenza and leprosy.

But for the PrP^Z to go airborne, it would need to be secreted into the oral cavity and/or respiratory tract in high enough numbers to cause infection. The prion would exist in the expelled droplets along with tiny bits of mucus and cellular material from the airways. The prion-infected droplets would hang in the air or deposit on surfaces until coming into contact with a new host.

This would merely be the first step; the next step is getting inside the cells of the host. For typical airborne transmission, such as the common cold (rhinovirus), the virus attaches to receptors on the cell surfaces of the upper airway, which trigger the cells to take in the virus like a Trojan horse. The PrP^Z prion would need to directly adhere to a cell surface or hitch a ride with another cell or organism that can. Once inside the cells, the prion would have to gain access to other areas of the body via the nerves or blood and lymph vessels to reach its final destination: the brain. This may be the easiest part; patients who contracted the vCJD (BSE) prion only had to eat one contaminated hamburger and somehow the PrP^{BSE} found its way from the GI tract to the brain. Once in the brain, PrP^Z would begin its terminal conversion of the normal PrP protein. Regardless of the exact mechanisms of how the prion would act on a molecular level, airborne transmissible disease would allow passage from person to person in a bus or airplane, eating food prepared by the infected or from exercise equipment at a gym.

Incubation Time: Rapid Infectivity and Clinical Symptoms

It is a must that the zombie disease must have a relatively short incubation time in order to become an apocalyptic threat. Yet we know that known prions have notoriously long incubation times, with most diseases incubating for several years before symptoms appear. Is it even possible for such a molecular change to occur and cause such huge functional differences? While one might think it would take an enormous amount of mutations to produce a prion that is airborne or one that rapidly acts in the brain, consider that human biology gives us examples of very small mutations that can result in big changes.

The classic example of the power of genetic mutation is sickle cell anemia. In sickle cell anemia the normally disk-shaped red blood cells (RBCs) become shaped like a sickle blade under certain conditions. This dramatic change—which can be fatal—arises due to a single 'point mutation' in the DNA. In patients with sickle cell anemia, only *one base* is mutated out of the 3 billion base pairs in a human DNA double helix. This tiny change results in an adenine (A) molecule changed to a thymine (T) within the gene sequence that codes for the beta subunit of the hemoglobin molecule. This almost imperceptible alteration in the DNA code changes one amino acid (from glutamate to valine) that causes the hemoglobin molecule to alter its oxygen-carrying function. This one-base change results in the symptoms of sickle cell anemia, which can cause severe pain and death. In other words, a massive change in function can occur from a tiny change in structure.

The mutation concept can be extrapolated to the world of virology, bacteriology and prion diseases. A mutation in the DNA that codes for the prion protein, or the way that the prion protein is processed within the cell, could produce the changes necessary to bring about the apocalyptic PrP^Z. Such mutations could lead to secretion into the oral cavity and respiratory tract or could promote a very rapid biological action of prion conversion within the brain. This could result in symptoms showing up in days instead of years. A period of days to weeks when the prion is being 'shed' by the infected individual would allow for the prion to come into contact with many other people without knowing it. Millions of people could be affected in a very short time frame. A prion that is easily transmissible, silently communicable and exerts its clinical effects in days instead of years sets the stage for the Zombie Apocalypse.

<u>Low Threat Level Agents: Parasites, Bacteria, Fungus and Amoeba</u>

<u>Parasites</u>

In common usage of the word, a parasite is something that lives in or on another species and benefits by obtaining nutrition from the host. The world of biology is filled with numerous examples of parasites in virtually all species, the most famous of which is probably the malaria parasite that is transmitted by mosquitoes. Parasites are also commonly transmitted to humans via improperly prepared food and contaminated drinking water. Some of these parasites seem to love taking up residence in the human brain, and as such must be examined as a potential zombiism cause.

One such parasite is *Toxoplasma.* The classic presentation for *Toxoplasma* is a patient with headaches and confusion who gets a CT-scan or MRI of the head and a brain mass is seen. When someone is diagnosed with a Toxoplasma brain lesion, it is diagnostic of immunosuppression and is considered an "AIDS-defining illness". The parasite is present in cat feces and is found immunosuppressed individuals who have cats or have been exposed to cat litter.

Taenia (the pork tapeworm) infections occur by eating undercooked pork. The eggs are ingested in the pork and the parasitic worms begin to grow in the small intestine. These worms can bore through the wall of the bowel, allowing them to gain access to the bloodstream where they can travel to the brain or the spinal cord. Once in the brain, the disease is referred to as 'neurocysticercosis', a medical term simply meaning 'cysts in the brain'. *Taenia* is believed to be the leading cause of seizures worldwide although is not common in developed nations.

Trypanosoma is another arthropod-borne disease spread to humans by the bite of the tsetse (pronounced 'tet-see' or 'teet-see') fly. Once the parasite is in the body it grows and proliferates for years, eventually causing African Sleeping Sickness. When the organism settles in the brain, it causes tremors, difficulty thinking, ataxia (difficulty walking) and personality changes.

Parasites are an interesting choice for the agent of zombiism because of their predilection for brain tissue. However, the threat level is very low because the symptoms of the diseases are not predictable or reproducible due to the random location of the parasites within the brain. One patient might have seizures while another might have blindness. Also diminishing the threat is that these diseases are not easily transmissible from human to human.

Bacteria

Some zombiologists have proposed a bacterial agent to be the cause of zombiism. These are considered to be low-level threats by most scientists because bacterial infections of the brain are typically too fast acting to produce any kind of meaningful zombie-like behavior. Patients often develop high fevers and may even rapidly lose consciousness such as in a case of bacterial meningitis. Bacterial infections of the brain are not self-limited, as these single-celled organisms will grow and reproduce as long as conditions are favorable for them to do so. Bacterial infections would produce such sickness that there would not be any capacity for the attacking behavior commonly seen in zombiism.

There is one distinct possibility where bacteria could be at the root of a zombiism outbreak: toxin-producing bacteria. Bacteria themselves can cause symptoms from their growth and reaction from our immune system, but some species can produce a protein toxin that carries out a specific action within the body. *Staphylococcus aureus* food poisoning involves a toxin that acts on the intestines to produce severe vomiting and diarrhea in as quickly as 30 minutes. Probably the most famous bacterial toxin is that of *Clostridium botulinum*, the organism that produces botulinum toxin. Although "BoTox®" has now become synonymous with cosmetic improvements of the skin, in higher concentrations, its muscle-paralyzing properties once made it a part of the U.S. biological warfare armamentarium. If a bacterium could produce a neurotoxin that can act on areas in the brain that are related to aggression, this could produce zombie-like behavior.

There are other types of infectious organisms such as fungus or amoeba, but these infections tend to be overwhelming, quickly producing the death of the patient. For instance, the amoeba *Naeglaria fowleri* lives in warm stagnant water, such as a pond in the southern United States. A swimmer may unintentionally inhale the amoebae-containing water, allowing it to access the brain from the nasal cavity. Once this happens, death is virtually certain.

Fungal infections of the brain are uncommon and may develop as an abscess in immunosuppressed patients. More commonly, fungus such as *Cryptococcus* and *Coccidioides* organisms can cause meningitis, and like amoebae and bacteria, fungal infections of the brain can be devastating and the patient is killed too quickly to manifest zombie-like symptoms. It is for this reason that bacteria, fungus and amoebae are very low risk in terms of producing Type 2 infectious zombiism.

While many different organism types have been proposed for a potential zombiism cause, many of these are not based in hard science. Simple predilection for the brain tissue is not enough to produce symptoms of aggression and attacking behavior. There must also be specificity of the biological agent while at the same time not doing so much damage to the host that death or unconsciousness occurs rapidly.

Zombie Epidemiology

This is not an epidemiology-focused text and many great works in the field of the epidemiology of zombiism are available online and in the scientific literature. For specifics in the mathematical models of the spread of zombiism, we suggest you read those sources. This section is merely an overview of epidemiological terms that are useful to describe how doctors and medical scientists might classify the zombiism outbreak and how the disease might present to the population.

An **endemic** disease is one confined to a characteristic place, group of people or related to a common activity. An example of an endemic disease is malaria, which tends to exist only in tropical regions such as sub-Saharan Africa because this is the best climate for mosquitos and the malaria (Plasmodium) parasite to thrive. New World zombiism could be endemic if it occurs in a group of people or a set geographic location. Certainly, chemical zombiism would most likely be endemic because it will likely arise from an impurity within a batch of drugs or the sharing of a common resource that is contaminated.

An **epidemic** disease is one that infects a larger number of people than is usually expected at any given time and has the propensity to spread to other geographic regions. A current example of an epidemic would be the return of measles to the populations of North America, Europe and Australia[7]. The *Night of the Living Dead* zombiism outbreak is considered to be an epidemic that occurred mostly in Pennsylvania and some other Midwestern states. There was no mention of it occurring beyond that area, and interestingly it appeared to have occurred over less than a 24-hour period. This would be a kind of 'flash epidemic' that could easily catch the public off-guard.

Beyond the epidemic is the **pandemic**. These "White Horse" apocalyptic disease candidates are outbreaks of an infectious disease that have worldwide distribution. The most recent pandemic we have faced is the H1N1 swine flu outbreak of 2009, which fortunately was not more lethal than usual types of flu. This also illustrates that a pandemic does not necessarily need to be excessively lethal, only that it is occurring in far more people and a broader geographical area than would be expected. The 20th century also saw at least three distinct influenza pandemics (1918, 1957, 1968) that killed 50 to 75 million people in total. Pandemic diseases tend to spread easily from person to person and have an incubation time and symptomatic period that is long enough to not burn out locally. In pop culture depictions, most stories focus on a group of survivors in a particular geographical region; therefore it is not possible to know if the disease is endemic or epidemic. However, one could reason that if only one country was affected, there would be some outside help to provide aid to survivors. Because we never see this it

---

[7] Normally there is a very low level of measles in the general population but due to the rise in numbers of unvaccinated citizens, new measles cases have far exceeded the baseline amount from what is usually expected.

is implied that most outbreaks of zombiism are indeed pandemic and extremely lethal in scope.

<u>Patient Zero and Pre-Pandemic Phase Zombiism</u>

The term "**Patient Zero (P_0)**" refers to the first known patient with the disease. It is impossible to accurately predict what a Patient Zero might be like in a disease we have not seen. Moreover, the P_0 is often determined long after an outbreak has started, when epidemiologists and other scientists track all the patients who had the disease. Investigators look for commonalities to narrow down who had the disease first, where it may have started and who that person may have been in contact with. The bird flu (1997) and SARS (2003) outbreaks in East Asia are examples of new diseases that required epidemiological tracking and mapping to identify P_0. Both diseases were highly lethal but were fortunately corralled as minor epidemics thanks to good public health practices and communication. Hopefully, this will be the case with an outbreak of zombiism. Because of the diseases unusual and violent features it will quickly make news and medical case reports. This will aid in stemming an outbreak and searching to identify the causative agent.

Myth vs. Reality: The Instant Apocalypse

One of the most terrifying aspects of fictional zombie outbreaks is the notion of the "instant apocalypse". In the instant apocalypse, the disease is transmitted person to person so fast that within a few days the population has been reduced to zombies and a handful of ragtag survivors. But how long would it really take for the world to descend into complete chaos from the first zombie patient to complete destruction of society? Is it possible to wake up one morning, turn on the news and see the whole world has transformed into endless hordes of infected zombies? While this makes for exciting fiction, it would be incredibly difficult for the world to collapse in such a short time. If the zombie disease is infectious, it is assumed that close contact is required in order to spread. Given this fact, there simply isn't enough time to infect sufficient amounts of people to spread the infection. Despite the possibility of a steep increase in zombies early in the outbreak, once the word got out that it was happening, people would take immediate shelter and enter a survival mode. This would rapidly decrease the infection rate and would allow time for law enforcement, the military and the public health apparatus to catch up and quash the outbreak.

***

The disease of zombiism, particularly Type 2, is one based on selective destruction or activation of certain areas of the brain that are responsible for aggression and related violent behaviors. The blueprint to how this might occur has been provided in the cases of the excited delirium due to drug intoxication. Such cases are considered reversible, so to rise to the level of an apocalyptic threat, the causative agent would need to act reproducibly and persistently (and quite possibly, permanently).

Science and medicine have identified numerous theoretical causes for zombiism that span the worlds of microbiology, biochemistry and even illicit drugs. But predicting what might cause the zombie apocalypse is a bit like predicting earthquakes: We know how they happen but we still can't predict where and when they will happen or their severity. Epidemiological factors such as rate of spread, method of transmission and population density will govern much about far the outbreak will go in consuming humanity.

PART III:

Zombie Injury, Neutralization & Weapons

When the time comes, forensic pathologists and their staff will be at the forefront of any zombiism outbreak. Because of the intense homicidal nature of zombies, pathologists will be tasked with the examination of the bodies to help determine the underlying cause of death. The realm of traumatic death and injuries are both squarely in the expertise of the forensic pathologist and we will examine the ways both humans and zombies are affected. Put another way: This section is about zombie killing.[8]

Weapons and Civil Defense: Neutralizing the Zombie Threat

The Great Weapons Debate

Its day 6 of the zombiism outbreak and you've been locked inside your house monitoring the situation virtually 24/7 on television, Internet or radio. Your activities to this point

---

[8] **"Killing" vs Neutralization**

As physicians, we do not condone violence in any way toward the dead or the living. Our group also prefers the term "neutralization" instead of "killing", not only because it lessens the murderous connotation but also because it more accurately includes the resurrected dead, which cannot technically be "killed".

include mostly laying low, peeking through your curtains in the daytime and trying to make as little noise as possible. You have been obsessively checking the locks on your doors and windows. You can hear them outside bumping into the side of the house, moaning and brushing past windows. The smell of death has crept into your home from the outside. But now you're running out of food and water and someone in your group is almost out of insulin; the time has come for you to leave to get supplies. But between you and the multiple city blocks you have to traverse, there are dozens, maybe even hundreds of roaming zombies. In your house you have a shotgun, a hunting bow with arrows, a baseball bat and a decorative samurai sword that is mounted on the wall. What weapon or weapons are your best choices to help you make it to your destination and back without getting yourself infected or killed?

Of all the elements of the zombie lore, questions on weapons and the best ways to "kill" a zombie are by far the most common questions I get as a forensic pathologist. Most people base their choices on what has been shown on TV or movies. For instance, crossbow purchases skyrocketed since *The Walking Dead* premiered in 2010. Although a crossbow might be a good weapon against one zombie, it is most certainly a terrible choice against a group of zombies. In the great weapons debate, most people only take one factor into consideration—killing power—but leave out a factor that's just as important: Preventing the spread of the infection and minimizing damage to bystanders. A gun, a sword or a baseball bat all have very different properties in terms of how they injure human tissue, and thus have different results on the creation of injuries and the spread of disease.

Zombie Type is the First Step in Weapon Choice

Before you grab your sword or hand cannon, you must be reasonably comfortable with the two major diagnostic types of zombies. Please refer to Part I of the book to review how to diagnose the type of zombie you might be dealing with. But why is this so critically important? The anatomical and physiological differences between the two major zombie types will guide your killing (ahem, neutralization) strategies.

Let's begin with the Type 1 zombies. These walking corpses have no basis for an infectious process. Reanimation cannot result from a microorganism such as a virus, because living tissue is necessary for this process. This will allow for a more aggressive approach by citizens who are trying to defend themselves. As the corpse decomposes, there will be dehydration of the tissues and the decrease in body fluids will lessen the amount of infectious blood or fluid spatter if violent force is used against the zombie. This is an oft-forgotten consequence of shooting guns or slashing at human tissues: blood and soft tissue can be quite messy. Although Type 1 zombiism is most likely not transmissible, any blood borne infectious diseases within the corpse still pose a threat to the living.

The real problem comes if the diagnosis is a Type 2 zombie; these zombies are still alive with blood being pumped at high pressure throughout the body. As such, any injuries to blood vessels can produce abundant infectious blood spatter. This is typically more of a problem with injuries to arteries because the blood pressure is higher in arteries than in veins. An arterial injury can produce jets of liquid blood corresponding to each beat of the heart and could instantly shower anyone nearby with warm, infectious blood. Fresh liquid blood may be packed with viruses, prions or any infectious organism the patient may have had prior to conversion.

If you aren't sure of the diagnostic type of zombie, it is best to err on the side of caution (and nonviolence) until the zombie agent is discovered. This of course could take quite a long time but the zombie type should be easy enough for experts to sort out and this information will be readily available through the Centers for Disease Control (CDC) website, your local health department and will certainly be well publicized through media outlets.

How Weapon Choice Affects the Spread of Infection

If you must act with violence to neutralize a zombie, the weapon of choice must be used responsibly. The following sections do not include every possible household item or weapon type that could be used to neutralize the zombie. Instead, the following sections are meant as examples of the most commonly available implements and the potential bodily damage done by those weapons. This will provide a basic understanding of the injuries and subsequent effects produced by different types of weapons on human/zombie tissues and will allow you to make the most sensible weapon choice should it become necessary.

Firearms

In television and movies, guns are far and away the most popular weapons to take out zombies. This is understandable given the accessibility of firearms and the high level of gun ownership (at least within the United States). The main benefit of a gun is that it allows one to have considerable distance between the zombie and the user, thereby decreasing infection risk from blood and tissue spatter. But there are also limitations to consider with this method. The first is "low hit rate". Pop culture depictions indicate that shooters hit their target zombie with almost supernatural accuracy. Few people in zombie TV shows or movies ever seem to miss their target. This does not reflect reality. Very few citizens are trained well enough to hit a moving target at distance, so it is more likely that several bullets might be expended to register one hit, which may not even be a fatal strike. If ammunition is limited (as it might be during the apocalypse) it could be rapidly expended, particularly in a situation with multiple zombies. This would tip the advantage to the zombie horde.

Ballistics & Gunshot Physics

Because the zombie anatomy and tissue properties are basically the same as a normal human, the effect on the organs and tissues would be the same as what is observed on the forensic pathologist's autopsy table. To begin to understand how bullets injure the body, one must have a grasp of ballistics and the basic physics of gunshot wounds.

Ballistics is the science of bullets and firearms and ultimately is a cross between physics and human biology. Key among ballistic factors in zombie neutralization is the **kinetic energy** of the bullet; kinetic energy is the energy of motion or movement of an object. When an unfired bullet is placed into a gun it has only potential energy, but the trigger pull sets into motion the process of conversion into kinetic and heat energy.

Upon the pull of the trigger, a firing pin hits the base of the bullet and causes a tiny explosion of the primer. The gunpowder is then ignited within the bullet cartridge, and so begins the gunshot. The combustion of gunpowder results in a massive increase in pressure, which forces the projectile away from the bullet cartridge. The **projectile** is the metal piece that actually leaves the gun but the terms 'projectile' and 'bullet' are often used interchangeably. See Figure 3.1 for bullet structure.

Figure 3.1. Bullet structure. © DL Wolfe.

As the gunpowder combustion continues to unfold behind the projectile, it continues to gain speed. The moment that the projectile leaves the muzzle, it has a predictable velocity for the type of weapon it was fired from. This **muzzle velocity** is in the physical sense the rate of change of position and direction of the bullet, but in common terms is simply how fast it's moving. Different types of guns have different muzzle velocities. With regards to tissue injury (zombie or otherwise), muzzle velocity is the single most important determinant. This is because the kinetic energy of the projectile is proportional to the degree of injury to the target, and velocity is the biggest factor in the amount of kinetic energy the bullet has. To understand why this is, observe the equation for kinetic energy:

Kinetic Energy (KE) =

½ (mass of the projectile) x (velocity of the projectile)^2

As demonstrated by the equation, the velocity of the projectile is squared (multiplied times itself), and without getting too mathematical this simply means that increases in velocity can result in much bigger increases in kinetic energy.

So why does the kinetic energy matter so much in tissue injury and why should we care? When a bullet impacts the body its kinetic energy will determine how deep it penetrates into or even through the body. As the projectile impacts and then moves through the body, injuries are produced in two ways: 1) Direct destruction from the bullet impact of anatomical structures 2) tissue destruction due to the **temporary cavity**. The temporary cavity is a kind of shockwave that causes tissues to expand rapidly, tearing them apart. Temporary cavities can explode skulls, completely destroy organs and shatter bones into multiple pieces.

Handguns typically have a lower muzzle velocity, in the range of 1,000-1,500 feet per second. Guns with long barrels, such as hunting rifles or assault-style rifles, produce muzzle velocities in the range of 3,000-4,000 feet per second. The shotgun, however, demonstrates that muzzle velocity isn't everything when it comes to injury. These weapons shoot projectiles that are heavier or have multiple small fragments and at short distance can produce injuries just as gruesome as the high velocity rifles. See Figure 3.2 for examples of gun types and muzzle velocities.

<u>Gun Type vs. Muzzle Velocity (General categories)</u>

Handgun	1,000 - 1,500 feet/second
Shotgun	900 – 1,300 feet/second
Rifles	2,500 - 4,000 feet/second

Figure 3.2. General ranges of muzzle velocity for commonly owned gun types.

While all this information may seem overly technical, the effects that certain guns have on the body of the zombie is essential information for which weapon you will choose and the manner in which you will use it. Because certain firearms can produce more explosive effects on a body, this has important implications on the distance you should keep from the zombie to minimize infection risk.

Recommended Range of Fire.

The **range of fire (RoF)** is defined as the distance from the muzzle of the gun to the target. In the world of forensics, the RoF is of immense importance in the investigation of gunshot wounds. By properly characterizing the appearance of a gunshot entrance wound, the RoF can help determine how far the shooter may have been from the person who was killed. The actual ways the forensic pathologist diagnoses RoF is not necessary for this discussion, but the ranges are important in general terms for the firearm user who may encounter zombies. For forensic purposes, the range of fire is divided into Contact, Close, Medium and Indeterminate ranges, based on the distance of muzzle to target. But for the purpose of zombie neutralization they will be grouped functionally based on the damage that might be done to the zombie.

Contact and Close Range

Contact range gunshot wounds are ones in which the gun barrel is physically touching the flesh of the human or zombie when the gun is fired. A contact gunshot to the head will most certainly produce the death of the zombie, but this has the unfortunate effect of infectious brain mist or blowback. **Brain mist**[9] is the liquid and particulate cloud of brain matter, cerebrospinal fluid and blood that may spray out of a contact gunshot wound or

---

[9] "Brain mist" is a term unique to the field of zombiology.

an 'explosive type' head wound. **Blowback** refers to the blood that sprays back onto the person holding the gun. Both brain mist and blowback markedly increase your risk of infection.

To demonstrate why the headshot increases infection risk, we must return to physics. When the muzzle of a discharged gun is in contact with the head, both the projectile (bullet) and the gases from combustion enter into the skull. The skull is a bony cavern with a fixed volume that cannot naturally expand. When the gases from the gun barrel enter the skull this results in a massive increase in intracranial pressure. In addition, if the muzzle velocity is high enough, the temporary cavity together with the increased pressure can produce an "explosive head wound". Such a wound will effectively neutralize the zombie but will spray everyone and everything within a several feet radius with brain mist and sharp bone fragments. This is more of a problem with rifles, shotguns and large caliber handguns.

As such, it is strongly recommended to avoid all contact gunshot wounds of the head in attempting to neutralize a zombie. Of note, rarely it has been depicted to put a gun in the zombie's mouth and fire the weapon. This is known as an intraoral gunshot and can produce the same type of explosive head wound. Other contact gunshot wounds, such as those to the chest and abdomen will not produce the explosive effect because the gases of combustion have room to expand inside these cavities.

Close range is similar to contact range, but the muzzle is not in complete contact with the skin. Close range is just outside of the skin up to of a few inches away from the target. While this distance is less likely to produce an explosive head wound, one can still get abundant brain mist and blood if the gun is a high velocity weapon such as a rifle.

Generally, if the zombie is within a foot of your weapon, there is an extremely high chance you will be sprayed with some amount of infectious spatter. If you are not wearing personal protective equipment such as masks or goggles, you risk becoming infected.

Medium, Indeterminate and Long Range

In forensics, "medium" range gunshots are those at a distance of approximately 6 to 30 inches (15 cm to 76 cm) from the muzzle to the target. This is what our group considers the '**minimum safe distance**' you would want to be from a zombie when firing the weapon. At medium range you still have stopping power but with less concern for blowback or brain mist. Beyond medium range, from around 3 feet to the absolute farthest distance from which the gun can hit the target, is considered to be 'indeterminate', in forensic terms. This means that beyond about 3 feet we simply cannot tell how far away the gun was from the target by looking at the wound; it could be 3 feet or 300 feet. Functionally, this is considered a long-range shot and is the recommended neutralization distance for any zombie.

Recommendations for Ideal Firearm Use

Distance: The number one principle in zombie neutralization is to maintain as much distance as you can between you and the target zombie. At a distance of several feet or more, the infection risk can be reduced to zero. Some guns are more accurate than others at long distances and keeping this in mind will help you minimize the use of ammunition. Rifles are typically more accurate at greater distance compared to shotguns or handguns due to longer barrels that produce a higher muzzle velocity. At higher velocity the projectile path is less affected by environmental conditions and gravity. In addition, it is recommended to use a weapon with a mounted scope. This will in theory produce more accurate shots and thereby saves ammunition.

Handguns produce a lower muzzle velocity and tend to be less accurate at long distances compared with rifles. Despite this shortcoming, the handgun is portable and can be used effectively at medium distances. A lighter weapon is recommended over a heavier one because of the decreased need to steady the gun to fire in a situation that might involve running or holding other objects. Small caliber handguns such as the .22 caliber or .25 caliber pistols can be quite light in the hand but the stopping power is questionable, especially in a non-fatal shot. The Type 2 zombies will likely manifest extreme aggression that is not easily diminished by minor gunshot injuries. As stated before, there are many examples of humans with excited delirium that have sustained multiple gunshots and still kept advancing. Thus, one must balance the appropriate gun caliber with gun size. A .38 caliber, 9 mm or .40 caliber handgun would suffice in stopping power and is light and small enough to keep on one's person. Any handgun of larger size and barrel length would have excellent stopping power but would be more difficult to carry in a survival situation, Rick Grimes notwithstanding.

The other type of common household firearm is the shotgun. The shotgun is a weapon often used by hunters or law enforcement due to its excellent stopping power. The shotgun can inflict a large amount of damage due to the bulk of the material that discharges from the shotgun shell. A shotgun shell contains either a large piece of metal (a slug) or multiple small pieces of metal like BB's ("shot"). The disadvantage of the shotgun is relatively low accuracy at distance compared with rifles. This necessitates the user to be at relatively close range to the zombie target, which thereby increases the risk of infectious spatter due to tissue destruction. Moreover, the size of the shotgun may make it difficult to handle in a situation that involves running and open combat. The best utility for shotgun use against an encroaching zombie might be a non-fatal shot to the legs, which would limit the creature's mobility while at the same time minimizing the amount of infectious spatter.

In general, it is advisable to be selective when using firearms. Random firing at zombies wastes precious ammunition and also risks injury to bystanders. In a world-ending survival situation, one will need as much cooperation with fellow humans as possible. Thus, it is best not to fire a weapon at a zombie if there is another person within 3 to 10 feet of the target; any closer could produce infectious spatter onto the bystander and cause injury or death. Also, it is not advisable to be out at night during an apocalyptic outbreak, but if it is absolutely necessary, it is an even worse idea to fire your weapon. With low visibility in darkness, one could accidentally shoot another human and in addition waste more ammunition because the target will be more difficult to see. The light and sound from any firearm could attract a zombie that might have not otherwise noticed you.

Sharp Force Weapons

Machetes, knives, hatchets, axes, samurai swords, arrows and many others can be used to produce what forensic pathologists refer to as 'sharp force injury'. This simply means that the weapons have a cutting edge or a sharp point that will produce the injuries. These are not ideal weapons to neutralize zombies because they require close distance combat, which markedly increases the risk of infection. However, the wide availability of these weapons means they will be commonly used during a zombie apocalypse.

Bladed weapons do have advantages. There is never a need to reload a blade-based weapon. There is also much less risk of injuries and infection to bystanders compared with inaccurate gunshots. For the purposes of defense against zombies, sharp force weapons can be divided into weapons that chop, stab, dismember and of course bow weapons.

Chopping Weapons

Weapons that chop include axes, hatchets or machetes. These weapons involve a heavy-handed move that produces a deep cut to the tissue as well as a blunt force component due to the weight of the weapon. These weapons can produce grotesque injuries that easily breach the skin and soft tissue and may fracture underlying bones. Such a wound may reach the depth of an artery and thus can produce copious infectious blood spray. Chopping weapons have great stopping power because of the devastating injuries they produce, but they must be used on the proper anatomical targets. Anatomical targets are discussed at the end of the chapter.

Stabbing/Cutting Weapons

Stabbing weapons such as knives and spears can be useful in producing painful injuries but close contact with the zombie is required. There is a much higher risk of injuring one's self while attempting to neutralize the zombie. Perpetrators who use knives to commit criminal stabbings often cut themselves on their own weapon as their hand slips past the hilt and onto the blade during the stabbing process. This could produce an open wound on the hand and thus increase infection risk from the zombie. Even if infection from the zombie is avoided, an unclean blade can cause a septic (blood) or wound infection. A gangrene infection would be most inconvenient for someone trying to survive an apocalyptic zombiism outbreak.

The best choice of the stabbing weapons is the spear. The spear has the advantage of delivering a forceful, impaling motion at a distance greater than that of any stabbing or chopping weapon and thus has less injury risk to the user. Spears are not in common use but it could be advisable to have one as part of your zombie defense collection.

Dismembering Weapons

Long-blade weapons such as swords or specialized axes can produce ghastly wounds to human tissue and can easily remove an arm, leg or head. This makes the long blade weapon an excellent choice to stop the zombie but risks an enormous amount of infectious blood spray. Our group has seen one individual killed with a samurai sword, and the body was cut almost completely in half with one stroke to the trunk of the victim. Due to the sharpness of the weapon there is complete cut of the vascular structures and the surrounding tissue. This has the effect of complete exposure of an artery without surrounding tissue obstructing it, unlike when a duller weapon is used. An unobstructed and open artery could spray infectious blood at high pressure, thus markedly increasing the risk of infection. Chainsaws are also included in the sharp force class of weapons, but these generate injuries more from ripping and shredding of tissue. We strongly advise against the use of a chainsaw because of the large amount of infectious spatter and tissue fragments generated by a motorized saw.

"Bow" Weapons:

Classic shooting weapons such as the hunter's bow and crossbow can be effective weapons for stopping a zombie. The two main advantages are accuracy of the weapon in skilled hands and the ability to incur a kill strike at a distance greater than minimum safe distance. These weapons are certainly an excellent choice against one or two rogue zombies because one can easily neutralize the creature, and then retrieve the arrow for future use. Against a horde of encroaching zombies this would be a poor weapon choice because of the limit of arrows that one can carry at any given time. Any lost arrow may be unrecoverable, thus leaving the user increasingly vulnerable to attack.

Blunt Force Weapons

Weapons that produce blunt injury are the most commonly available weapons in the home of the unprepared citizen. Baseball bats, golf clubs, hammers and other such weapons can be used to thwart zombie attack. These methods share some of the same drawbacks as bladed weapons, such as the need to be close to the target. Significant force is usually needed to produce injury, which is typically in the form of lacerations. Laypersons and medical professionals often incorrectly equate "laceration" with a cut. A cut is produced by something with a sharp edge like a knife, razor blade or broken glass. Lacerations are actually formed from the breakage of the skin by impact with a flat or rounded object. When involving the head, these injuries can also produce a large amount of blood spatter and what is known as "cast-off". **Cast off** is blood or tissue that flies off the weapon when drawing it away from the target after the impact. Both blood spatter and cast off may result in infection risk both for the individual with the weapon and people in the vicinity. Therefore, bludgeoning (beating to death with a blunt weapon) is not a recommended neutralization technique unless you actively want to become infected with the zombiism agent.

The best utility for blunt weapons may be in producing temporary incapacitation such as blows to the knees or shins that can result in immobility and pain. Secondly, a blow to the abdomen or chest can produce temporary loss of breath by the living zombie and could buy valuable time in getting away.

Fire

Despite the increased availability of commercially available flamethrowers, this is not a good way to neutralize zombies. Fire is hypothetically the best method because of maximal stopping power due to incineration of the creature while also destroying the infectious agent. Some have suggested the use of Molotov cocktails (a glass bottle containing an accelerant with a lit rag stuffed into the opening of the bottle) as a makeshift weapon. Such methods could be used as a deterrent or to buy time to get away from a zombie. The downside of course, is that one could produce an out of control fire in a closed space (such as in a house or apartment) and risk potential of serious burn injury or carbon monoxide poisoning. In rural areas this could produce the destruction of acreage and property. An out of control fire can also limit escape possibilities.

Zombie Defense: Advanced Anatomical Target Strategies for Neutralization

Wounds of the Head

Because the skull does not have uniform thickness throughout, there are some areas that are more vulnerable to injury than others. The following anatomical areas of the skull are recommended for best results. Please see Figure 3.3.

Temporal Strike. At the sides of the head just above the ears are the temporal areas of the scalp. This area includes the skin, subcutaneous tissue, temporalis muscles and the temporal bones of the skull. The anatomy of the temporal bone is widely varied in shape and thickness but the area between the ear canal and the outside edge of the eye socket presents an excellent target for neutralization. This is known as the squamous portion of the temporal bone and can be only 2 or 3 millimeters thick in adults. This is about the thickness of 15 pieces of stacked paper and is an ideal target for any type of weapon (firearm or other) to penetrate into the skull and transgress into the brain.

Midface Strike. Another excellent anatomical target is right through the middle of the face. One must aim for the nose as the target, as this area is largely composed of cartilage, a material much softer than bone. Past the soft tissue of the nose there is an opening (the nasal cavity) that allows for direct access to the skull base, through which a projectile or blade can more easily enter into the cranial vault. Although it is more difficult to traverse the thick bone of the skull base, there are many vital structures such as the circle of Willis arteries and the structures of the midbrain/brainstem that control breathing and heart rate.

Ocular Strike. The bones of the orbit are actually quite thin relative to the rest of the skull. In some areas, these bones (known as the orbital plates) can be only about 1-2 millimeters in thickness. In head injuries of any type, this is the most frequently broken bone of the skull. In fact, these areas often manifest what are called "eggshell fractures" because the delicate cracks seen on this bone look like a broken chicken's egg. If a projectile or weapon enters at the eye, there is full access to the frontal lobe of the brain, the brain base and depending on the angle, the brainstem. Another advantage of this approach is that it also will decrease the vision of the zombie by 50%, which will limit its attacking power.

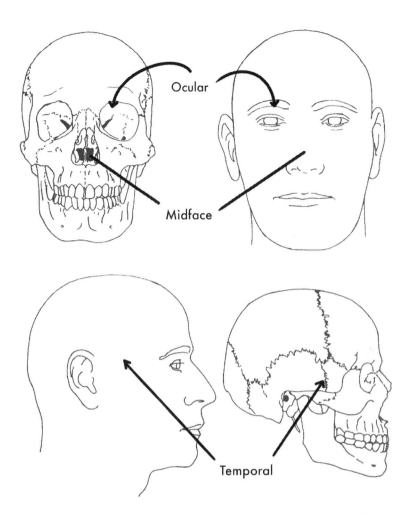

Figure 3.3. Anatomical Areas of the Skull for Neutralization. *Midface* and *Ocular* strikes (top) and *Temporal* strike (bottom). © DL Wolfe.

Wounds of the Neck.

Although virtually never demonstrated in zombie fiction, an alternative approach to taking out zombies is to aim for the neck. A Type 2 zombie will operate within the parameters of the human vascular, neurological and musculoskeletal systems. Thus, a well-placed shot into the neck has a high probability of hitting a vitally important anatomical structure that can cause immediate stoppage of the creature. A bullet that passes through the neck has a high likelihood of producing injury to the spinal cord. This may occur either by direct passage of the bullet or by shattered fragments of the vertebral body, which are razor sharp bone shrapnel. Spinal cord injury will render all muscles below the level of the injury nonfunctional, thus stopping movement of the limbs. At the level of the third to fifth cervical vertebrae (C3-C5) is the emergence of the phrenic nerve, which sends its fibers to the diaphragm. The diaphragm is the flat muscle that separates the chest from the abdomen and is essential to the process of breathing. An injury to this area of the spinal cord would thus paralyze the diaphragm and the zombie could no longer breathe. Without breathing air there is no oxygen exchange, and this results in incapacitation and death.

On each side of the neck are the carotid arteries and jugular veins. See Figure 3.4. The carotid artery is about the diameter of a pencil and the jugular vein is about the diameter of your pinky finger. The carotid artery delivers blood under high pressure to the brain whereas the jugular vein drains blood at low pressure and delivers it back to the heart. One need not injure both vessels to produce death. If the carotid artery is injured there are two major effects: 1) the blood supply to the brain is interrupted and 2) the blood may spurt from the neck quickly. Both effects are desirable in stopping the zombie, since blood pressure would begin to decrease as blood is lost from the carotid. One must be careful, because this type of wound is not immediately fatal and could produce a last ditch episode of maximal aggression from the zombie. If delivering a nonfatal wound to the neck, it is advisable to get to safety as quickly as possible to avoid being attacked by the only thing worse than a regular zombie: A panicked zombie with blood spraying from its neck.

The optimal neck wound would be that of a chopping weapon to the back of the neck. This method would result in fracture of the vertebral bodies and a severed spinal cord. This would neutralize the zombie and has the benefit of a decreased risk of arterial blood spatter. The neck chop would likely sever vertebral arteries but they are of relatively small diameter and are deep within the neck, thus decreasing the likelihood of blood spraying from the wound.

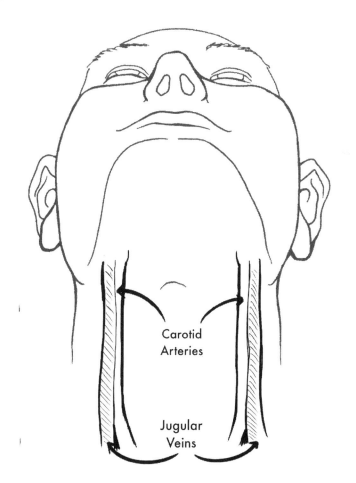

Figure 3.4. Largest blood vessels in the anterior neck: the common carotid arteries and the internal jugular veins. © DL Wolfe.

Wounds of the Trunk (Chest and Abdomen)

The heart is an excellent target for neutralization. Just like in normal humans, the Type 2 zombie must have a functional circulatory system with the heart pumping oxygen-rich blood to the rest of the body. An aggressive zombie would have an increased heart rate and blood pressure due to the hyperactive state. The trunk is also the largest area of the body, which is why armed professionals are trained to aim for the trunk when attempting to neutralize a hostile suspect. There are many vital structures within the chest such as the heart, aortic arch, the superior and inferior vena cava, pulmonary arteries, thoracic aorta and of course the lungs. A penetrating injury to any of these structures can produce death in short order. However, the chest is much more difficult to breach with a sharp or blunt weapon because of the protective rib cage. The chest is a more ideal target for a firearm injury.

Subxiphoid Strike.

If you are without a firearm, the best area to aim for is what is called the "subxiphoid" area. This refers to the area just below the lowest portion of the sternum (breastbone). If one uses an impaling weapon at an upward angle versus a zombie at close range, this will give adequate access to the heart, lungs, and large vessels that emerge from the heart. This will dramatically increase your odds of landing a fatal strike. See Figure 3.6.

Abdominal wounds. The abdomen is very vascular (having many blood vessels). As such, a bullet passing through the abdomen has a high likelihood of rupturing a large blood vessel such as the abdominal aorta, portal vein or inferior vena cava. While this may not produce immediate stoppage of the creature, it could produce fatal internal bleeding in a short amount of time. Because the chest and the abdomen are both cavities, blood tends to fill these spaces instead of spurting outward from the body. Chest and abdomen injuries would thus have a lower risk of infectious spatter and are good targets for neutralization if the zombie is at close range.

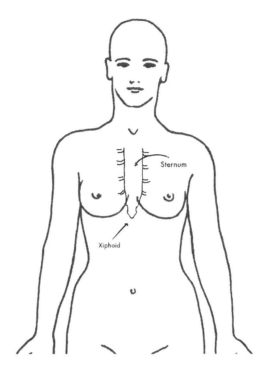

Figure 3.6. The area of the *subxiphoid* strike. © DL Wolfe.

The discussion of these neutralization techniques and weapons is merely considered an overview. There are hundreds and even thousands of different combinations of "weapon vs. anatomical site" that could be used to good effect in the right hands. But as we choose our weapons we must also consider the zombie type to minimize the risk of infection. This chapter was constructed mainly with the Type 2 (living) zombies in mind. The prepared citizen should have a plan for both resurrected dead (Type 1) zombies as well. Despite this discussion (which is sure to produce great debate), it is still recommended to not engage the zombie threat. This will minimize casualties and infection risk as well as reduce the possibility of future legal problems from killing a zombie. The resurrected dead are not considered to be an infectious entity, so the focus of neutralization would be more about preventing the encroaching zombie from getting closer. Injuries that would normally be fatal in the Type 2 zombie may have no effect on the Type 1 zombie. In this case, one can default to the time-honored headshot.

The Head Shot Myth: A Dangerous Tactic

One common motif seen in almost all zombie fiction is that destroying the head is the *only* way to stop the creature. While it is true that destroying the head of any creature is pretty effective in stopping it, the ways in which this has been depicted are misleading and can even be dangerous. For instance, there is a notion that simply entering the cranial vault is like hitting an "off" switch for the zombie. How many times have we seen a merciful hero gently press a knife into the skull and instantly kill the zombie?

Unlike what has been depicted, the skull is not the consistency of paper mache. Even a Type 1 zombie that is hundreds of years old would still have the same basic level of skull hardness as the freshly dead. An attempt to stab into the skull is much more likely to produce injury of the person with the knife than it is to the zombie. The act of stabbing often causes the hand to slip forward onto the blade, which is why individuals suspected of having committed a stabbing are examined for cuts to their own hands. If one is dealing with a Type 1 (resurrected) zombie, the brain could be either completely liquefied in the decomposing corpse or virtually absent in older zombies. There is also no discernible blood flow in the Type 1 zombie. Without blood coursing through blood vessels of the brain there is no concern for increased risk of death due to bleeding within the skull. To enter the skull would produce no discernible internal injury and thus there is no rationale for a headshot producing death in the Type 1 zombie.

***

Zombie neutralization is a field of study that goes far beyond the simplistic 'universal head shot'. Ultimately, we must remember that zombies are anatomically human and at least among Type 2 zombies, also physiologically human. This knowledge provides some guidance on where to attack and the consequences of the physical disruption of the zombie body. By employing the best techniques suited to a particular weapon, one can markedly decrease the risk of infection and the unintentional harm done to bystanders. Proper neutralization techniques hinge on the correct diagnosis of Type 1 versus Type 2 zombie along with sane (and conservative) weapon usage.

PART IV:

Zombie Autopsy, Discovery and Case Studies

The early part of the zombie apocalypse—before it's an actual apocalypse—will involve a lot of autopsies. An **autopsy** is the postmortem medical and surgical examination that will be used to examine bodies during the outbreak to determine exactly what might be causing the homicidal behavior, whether it is an infectious organism, an unusual chemical or something completely unforeseen.

Contrary to popular belief, few people that die actually undergo autopsy. In fact, among patients that die in a hospital, less than 5% are referred for an autopsy. An outbreak of zombiism would indeed result in a much higher percentage of autopsies because the vast majority would be unexplained, unexpected or violent deaths. Such deaths are the realm of the forensic autopsy, which aims to certify the cause and manner of death for each individual. The **cause of death** is the specific medical reason why the person has died. Examples include things like "gunshot wound to chest", "blunt force trauma of the head" or "Complications of Type 2 Zombiism". The **manner of death** is the group within which the death can be categorized. The five categories of death used by forensic pathologists are "natural", "accident", "suicide", "homicide" and when there is insufficient information, "undetermined".

The legal system would require pathologists to perform autopsies on any unexpected death during the outbreak whether it was due to a zombie or not. In the pre-apocalyptic period, the forensic pathologist would have to answer such questions as:

1) Did the decedent have zombiism?

2) Did the death occur as a result of zombiism or as a result of neutralization?

3) Did the decedent die of a natural disease or from an accident or suicide?

4) If the decedent did not have zombiism, accident or other natural diseases, is the death a homicide?

In the history of new or emerging diseases, the autopsy has been of critical importance in elucidating the cause and effects of the disease within the body. Infectious diseases such as Zika virus, HIV/AIDS and SARS (Severe Acute Respiratory Syndrome) virus are just a few examples of diseases that were thoroughly investigated and characterized with autopsies. Forensic autopsy is at its essence, all about discovery. When faced with an uncertain new disease or suspicious cause of death, epidemiologists, clinical and research teams and pathologists must work together to uncover the nature of the disease. In the case of zombiism, there would be great fear and uncertainty in the public. Forensic specialists would be on the frontlines, uncovering information about the outbreak to help protect the public. But how long might it really take to discover the unknown agent that is causing zombiism? In the past, we have had to face the rapid discovery of a novel human disease many times, but none was so pressing as the discovery of HIV/AIDS. The saga provides a template on how an outbreak can unfold and how we can work together to shine light on a new disease entity.

Lessons from the Past: The Timeline of Discovery for HIV

The emergence of HIV/AIDS was one of the most culture-defining events of the 20th century. The story of discovery began on June 5, 1981 when the publication *Morbidity and Mortality Weekly Report* described five (5) cases of an unusual pneumonia that was caused by an organism known as *Pneumocystis carinii* (now called *Pneumocystis jiroveci*) in previously healthy gay men in Los Angeles, California. This yeast-like fungal infection was known to occur in patients with extremely depleted immune systems. On the exact same day, a New York based dermatologist called the CDC to report a cluster of cases of Kaposi sarcoma in gay men. Kaposi sarcoma is a cancer of small blood vessels that is caused by a virus (Human Herpesvirus-8). A cancer caused by a virus also seemed to hint at a failing immune system in the affected patients.

As the weeks and months progressed, more medical professionals experienced similar findings all over the country. Tens of cases became hundreds, hundreds became thousands and eventually millions were discovered to have the disease. A new epidemic was upon us and no one knew the cause.

Researchers worked around the clock to find the underlying cause for this syndrome that appeared to destroy the human immune system. Despite a focused multinational effort on the unknown disease, it took over *2 years* to identify the causative agent. In 1983, Dr. Françoise Barre-Sinoussi and Dr. Luc Montagnier of the Pasteur Institute (France) announced the discovery of a retrovirus that was the cause of AIDS. The virus did not actually get its official name—the Human Immunodeficiency Virus (HIV)—until 1986, *five years* after the first case was reported.

A zombiism epidemic would trigger immediate research but it is very unlikely that we would be able to maintain a functioning society for two years while scientists search for the cause. But there are advantages we have today that did not exist in the early 1980s. The molecular biology testing is far more advanced and diverse than what existed then. There are many more hospitals and research facilities dedicated to the investigation of new infectious diseases. Perhaps most importantly, today's means of communication is instantaneous and global, due to the advent of the Internet, social media and messaging apps. As a result, clinical features of zombiism would be well described and autopsy findings would be quickly reported. Such rapid communication between expert scientists around the globe would help make accurate predictions about the types of infectious biological agents that could cause the disease. Even with the diagnosis in hand, there would still be questions about how the disease could be transmitted, how long it incubates and its exact cellular biology.

***

We now present case studies simulating how the disease would present to a primary care physician or Emergency Department. During a real zombiism outbreak, doctors and other health care providers would be presented with an unusual set of symptoms and would have to make decisions on treatment and test ordering without knowing the diagnosis. For all patients that die, an autopsy would be ordered, particularly early in the outbreak before the cause is known. These case studies also aim to describe the autopsy procedure in reasonable detail to give the reader a sense of how the autopsy aids in discovery, and also illustrates the many precautions one would need to take during this potentially dangerous procedure.

The Autopsy of Ms. Flair, The Infectious Zombie

Case Notes and Dictation by Dr. Ciardullo

"It's day 22 of the outbreak. The CDC still doesn't know how the disease is spread but early reports indicate that body fluids including blood, urine and saliva contain the organism. Early estimates indicate that hundreds and perhaps thousands have already contracted the disease. Today's case is our eighth suspected zombiism autopsy since the outbreak began.

Ms. Flair is an unfortunate 26-year-old female who was a surgical technician at Nelson County Hospital. An unconscious and critically ill patient had been brought in two days prior after an apparent self-inflicted gunshot wound. He had survived the initial gunshot and underwent surgery to remove part of the skull in order to decrease intracranial pressure. While in surgery, Ms. Flair nicked her left index finger with a scalpel. According to medical records, the wound was only 4 millimeters in length and she did not need stitches. She was treated with antibiotics and antiviral medications. Approximately three days after the injury she missed work and did not respond to texts or phone calls. This was uncharacteristic, so her manager (Ms. Pinel) asked that local police conduct a check of her wellbeing. She was not in her apartment. The scene photos indicated that her living space was in complete disarray. Blood was smeared on walls and in the bathroom but there was no indication of high velocity blood spatter. For four days her whereabouts were unknown. On the 5th[th] day after her scalpel injury, she was seen three miles from her apartment in the Autumn Hills Subdivision. A man was with his two children in the backyard, when Ms. Flair emerged from a section of woods to the south of the home. She was disheveled and stumbling toward the yard.

Then, upon seeing him and the children, she broke into a full sprint and leapt a short chain-link fence and proceeded to attack. The man was able to get the children to safety and call 9-1-1, but he was also injured in the process, suffering scratches to his neck and face and a bite to his right shoulder. Police officers responded to the scene, and Ms. Flair then rushed at the officers. Pepper spray was deployed but had no effect. A second officer drew his gun and shot Ms. Flair twice, killing her. Her body was brought to the Handley County Morgue for an autopsy."

***

There are inherent risks of doing an autopsy procedure on a patient with an infectious disease. The freshly dead still harbor any biological agent that may have already been in the blood and tissues, such as hepatitis viruses or HIV. Infectious diseases such as influenza, tuberculosis or Ebola are easily transmitted during autopsy if proper procedures are not used. It is not a stretch to believe that infectious zombiism could pose the same threat.

Autopsy Procedure

While most people immediately think of the gory details of the surgical portion of the autopsy, the external examination is the first part of the procedure. The external exam provides a wealth of information about the decedent and is meant to document the body exactly as it was received in the morgue. Photographs are taken and trace evidence on the body is collected. Identifying characteristics such as surgical scars, tattoos, piercings and hair and eye color are noted. Death signs such as the degree of rigor mortis, pattern of livor mortis or signs of decomposition are noted, and of course the presence or absence of injuries.

"The body is received intact but injuries are present. There are indeterminate range gunshot wounds to the right side of the head and of the mid-chest. The hair is brown and medium length, and matted with blood and brain matter. The eyes are hazel in color and the pupils are dilated to 8 millimeters. The eyes appear bloodshot. The nose is normal but the mouth is injured and there is blood on the chin. Multiple lacerations are present on the inner surface of the lips and of the tongue. There are multiple missing and broken teeth. There is blood in the ear canals and the ears have multiple piercings. The body is clothed in light blue hospital scrubs, which are soiled with dirt and fresh and dried blood. The clothing is removed. There are no surgical scars but there is a tattoo of the word "Eme" on the left arm. There are no possessions with the body.

Strong rigor mortis is present in the extremities. Livor mortis is located on the posterior surface of the body, consistent with supine position after death. The livor is pink-purple in color and blanches when compressed. The body is cool to the touch. There are no signs of decomposition. There are no distinct odors. Examination of the limbs reveals multiple broken fingernails as well as scratches and small cuts to the hands and wrists. A healing injury is seen on the left index finger, consistent with history of scalpel injury."

The external examination was consistent with someone who had been outdoors for quite awhile, as evidenced by the clothes soiled with dirt. The injuries were both superficial and fatal. Signs of attacking behavior could have been inferred even without the reported history. She had broken nails due to clawing and scratching but most compelling was her mouth exam, because the lacerations to lips and tongue plus broken or missing teeth indicates that very likely, Ms. Flair had bitten someone or some thing in the interval after she had gone missing, possibly infecting others.

<u>Internal Examination</u>

The internal examination is a surgical procedure that allows visual inspection and removal of the internal organs of the head, neck, chest, abdomen and pelvis. This is the part of the autopsy that carries the most risk to the dissector and others in the room.

"The body is opened with a Y-shaped incision, with the top part of the Y starting at each shoulder and meeting in the center of the chest. A linear incision is extended over the abdomen to the front of the pelvis. The ribs and the bowel loops of intestines are exposed and easily visualized. The liver, stomach, pancreas and spleen appear normal. To gain access to the organs of the chest, the sternum ("breastbone") and attached ribs are removed."

This "chest plate" can be removed with different methods, all of which have their own possible infection risks. A common method of removal uses pruning shears like ones used for cutting small branches in the garden. But when cutting the ribs with this method, a frayed edge of the bony rib can result in razor sharp, needle-like fragments of bone that can easily poke through a glove or sleeve. Another method uses an electric bone saw that results in clean, dull rib edges but can produce airborne bone dust that could contain an infectious agent. Making matters worse, if there is blood in the chest cavity, it may spray onto dissectors while the bone saw vibrates the chest. Once the chest plate is removed, all organs from the neck to the pelvis can be visualized and surgically dissected.

Even the cleanest autopsy practitioners will finish an evisceration with blood soaked gloves and sleeves. This gives ample opportunity to become infected if there is a small knick in one's glove or blood was to seep through a gown (particularly at the wrist). But with good preparation and great care taken during the autopsy, there should be no infections during the internal examination of the body.

It is the procedure of opening the head that would produce the greatest risk of infection in a zombiism case, particularly if a prion is the suspected cause. In a case with a possible prion or other unknown deadly agent, the staff would have to wear what many medical examiners refer to as the "space suit". This is similar in appearance to what researchers wear when dealing with deadly "hot zone" type diseases in Biosafety Level 4 laboratories. The space suit goes beyond the usual gown and gloves and instead covers the entire body. The dissector then breathes air through a filter that removes all possible harmful infectious agents.

"An incision is made from the right mastoid area behind the ear over the top of the head to the left mastoid area. The scalp is folded forward over the brow and the back of the scalp is reflected posteriorly. There is abundant blood in the subcutaneous tissue and within the right temporalis muscle due to the gunshot wound. Linear fractures are seen extending onto the right parietal bone and frontal bone. There is brain matter extruding from the entrance of the skull at the right temporal bone."

Infectious prions are thought to be present in all tissues and fluids, but exist in high concentrations within the brain, spinal cord and cerebrospinal fluid. The electric bone saw is used to cut through the skull by both pressure and high frequency oscillation of the blade. When the saw is maneuvered through the skull, little puffs and eddies of tan-colored bone dust enter into the air around the head of the corpse. One can smell the freshly ground bone, which has an odor like singed hair. The dust settles due to gravity, covering everything in the vicinity of the head with a barely perceptible layer of potentially infectious dust. Inadequate eye or facial coverage by the dissector would risk exposure to the bone dust. Another drawback of opening the head with a bone saw is blood spray if there is excess blood in the cranial vault. This is often the case when the brain has been injured and a subdural or subarachnoid hemorrhage is present. It is for this reason that the skull be opened inside of a bag to diminish the presence of infectious bone dust or liquid droplets in the air.

"The calvarium is removed to reveal an acute subdural hemorrhage is present, more prominent on the right cerebral hemisphere than the left side. A circular defect is present on the right temporal portion of the dura, consistent with passage of a bullet. The dura is removed to further reveal blood on the surface of the brain in the form of subarachnoid hemorrhage. The brain itself has an unusual appearance for the age of the patient. There is an overall degenerated look, with each convolution appearing thin and the sulci (grooves) appearing widened consistent with brain atrophy. A medium-caliber bullet is present on the surface of the left cerebral hemisphere. This bullet is collected and turned over to the police evidence technician.

The brain is removed by cutting the attachments of the optic nerves, pituitary gland and the vascular and nerve structures at the base of the brain. Fractures of the skull base are present. Because of the very unusual appearance of this brain, it will be fixed in formalin

and examined with the neuropathologists, Drs. Valadez and Belduis.

The cause of death is Multiple Gunshot Wounds and the manner of death is Homicide.

Pending review of the brain, it is likely that Type 2 Zombiism caused by a prion can be

considered a contributing factor to her irrational and attacking behaviors."

In the known types of prion diseases the brain can take more than a year after symptoms

to show end stage changes such as severe brain atrophy. But in a Rapidly Infective Prion

(RIP) such as what was described in Part II of this book, the infection and symptom

timeline would be markedly shortened. The damage would progress swiftly, producing

changes in just days or weeks that might usually take ten times as long.

The atrophy noted by the pathologist refers to 'wasting away' of the brain tissue. This is

commonly seen in other neurodegenerative diseases such as Alzheimer's Disease and

prion diseases like CJD and vCJD. Once the brain is removed, it may be sliced

immediately and tissue samples taken to look at in the microscope. In cases with a

suspected brain disease such as zombiism, it would first be placed in a formaldehyde

solution for weeks. This fixation process causes the brain to be firm, which makes for

easier cutting and examination by the pathologist. More precise anatomical samples can

be taken and then viewed in the microscope to look for changes that cannot be seen with

the unaided eye. With the RIP, one would see the classic 'spongiform' change from the

many holes that are seen in the cells and brain tissue. These 'holes' are actually small

vacuoles (empty spaces) that have a 'Swiss cheese' appearance.

***

Autopsies in the setting of a zombiism outbreak would include those with the zombie disease but anyone else who would have died. This seems superfluous in the setting of 'apocalypse' but consider that early in the outbreak the public would likely not realize the full implications of the outbreak and what is to come. Patient cases can be divided among those that occur before society descends into a chaotic apocalyptic pandemic (the 'early apocalypse') and those cases that occur after it is probably too late for the public health apparatus to fully thwart the outbreak. Deaths occurring after the apocalypse is in full swing will likely not be investigated by autopsy, with the exception of a few government facilities (if there are people still alive to run them). Causes and manners of death during a zombie apocalypse will be wide-ranging. While we have been conditioned to think mostly of the widespread murderous attacks of zombie hordes, there would be many other ways that people would die. The following cases are meant to reflect the reality of the heterogeneity of cases that would be seen by clinical doctors and pathologists.

Early Apocalypse Case 1: Mr. Edwards Prison Release

Mr. Edwards is a 39-year-old male that was recently released from prison. Approximately 72 hours after his release he was witnessed to manifest extreme aggression at a local convenience store. He was destroying property within the store and attacked the clerk, who was able to get away with only minor injuries. Mr. Edwards was then seen sprinting down the street for about three city blocks before slowing down, falling to his knees and clutching his chest. EMTs responded but Mr. Edwards was already dead. His body was brought to the Briscoe Memorial Hospital morgue for autopsy.

Autopsy Results, (Dictation: Dr. Bassett):

"There was minor external trauma to the body including small cuts, abrasions and contusions throughout. He was in otherwise good physical condition. The internal examination revealed some hepatomegaly (liver = 2,250 grams, normal ~1,600 grams) and abnormalities of the heart. The left anterior descending coronary artery had a 90% occlusion of atherosclerosis. Sectioning of the heart muscle revealed a pale yellow area in the anterior left ventricle consistent with an acute myocardial infarction. The examination of the brain revealed a normal surface appearance and there were no hemorrhages or indications of atrophy. Microscopic examination of the brain did not reveal inclusions or spongiform changes."

Toxicology: Positive for methamphetamine, amphetamine and cocaine.

Cause and Manner of Death: Mr. Edwards suffered an acute myocardial infarction as a result of atherosclerotic occlusion in a major coronary artery. This was very likely made worse by methamphetamine[10] and cocaine consumption after being released from prison. The strain on the heart caused increased oxygen demand and the occluding plaque decreased the amount of blood effectively getting to the heart muscle. The heart had been sectioned to show an area of the heart muscle that was dead. The pale yellow appearance indicates this infarct was a few days old and likely started around the time he was released from prison. The absence of suspicious viral or prion changes in the brain rules out infectious zombiism. This was a case of true excited delirium due to drug intoxication, which also contributed to the development of the heart attack (acute myocardial infarction). This death was natural. Although the drug intoxication made it

---

[10] The presence of amphetamine is due to the breakdown of methamphetamine in the body, to methamphetamine and amphetamine.

worse, the timeline suggests the heart attack was in process before he was released from prison.

<u>Early Apocalypse Case 2: Mr. Chaves Unfortunate Attack</u>

Mr. Chaves was a 27-year-old male that had recently traveled on business from Dublin, Ireland to Chicago, IL. While waiting for transportation at the airport he was attacked by a disheveled woman and he sustained superficial scratches to the face and neck. No additional therapy was needed. A bystander that helped with the incident reported that the woman (referred to only as 'Rosie' by police) had copious saliva dripping from her mouth and it may have dripped into the mouth or eyes of Mr. Chaves. About two days later, he developed confusion, paranoia, and personality changes. After he started spitting saliva constantly, he was taken to the Emergency Department by his fiancé. He developed increasing aggression to which sedatives had no effect. At the point when he was about to be restrained and admitted for psychiatric hold, he broke free, fought through several hospital staff and ran into the streets. About an hour later, he was seen attacking a homeless person in a public park. The victim sustained many bites and avulsions of the head and neck. Officers responded to the scene and fired on Mr. Chaves, ending the attack. His body was brought to the morgue for autopsy.

<u>Toxicology:</u>   Negative.

<u>Autopsy Results (Dictation by Dr. Desboeufs):</u>

"Mr. Chaves has a fairly healthy overall appearance but the eyes are sunken possibly due to dehydration. There is abundant red-tan foam seen at the nose and the mouth. There are injuries to the mouth and several teeth are missing. Multiple gunshot wounds are

present to the chest, abdomen and extremities. Internal examination revealed bullet injury to the liver and the abdominal aorta. Two hollow point projectiles are recovered and turned over to the police evidence technician. The uninjured organs have a normal appearance. The skull is opened to reveal a fairly normal brain although the blood vessels on the surface of the hemispheres are somewhat congested. Sections of the brain are reviewed under the microscope and reveal chronic inflammation around blood vessels and inclusion bodies within the Purkinje cells of the cerebellum. These inclusions are similar to what are called Negri bodies in rabies."

Cause and Manner of Death:

It is clear that the cause of death is multiple gunshot wounds and the manner of death is homicide. Because Mr. Chaves was engaged in a vicious attack on another citizen and showed no signs of stopping, this would likely be ruled a justifiable homicide. He showed signs like excited delirium but also had increased salivation. The attack at the airport was minor but his attacker infected him with saliva. The autopsy results confirmed the gunshot wound injuries but the brain exam was consistent with infection with a Rabies-Like Virus (RLV). Hence, although the cause of death was multiple gunshot wounds and the manner was homicide, Mr. Chaves suffered from RLV infection, a form of Type 2 zombiism. Although zombiism would have ultimately been fatal, the gunshot wounds were what immediately caused the death.

Early Apocalypse Case 3: Ms. Bryson and an Infected Corpse

Ms. Bryson was a 23-year-old female mortuary science student who was helping to prepare a body for burial at the Barton Funeral Home. The body had been autopsied one day prior at Perry Memorial Hospital, reportedly for an unspecified neurodegenerative disease. While adjusting the chest plate that had been removed during autopsy, she got a small cut on the palm of her hand. She immediately washed her hands, attempted to squeeze blood from the wound and even poured bleach on her hand multiple times. Approximately 48 hours later, she attacked several patrons at a restaurant not far from her apartment. She then ran into the street and was struck by a car. She got up and continued to sprint and finally collapsed two blocks away. She was pronounced dead at the scene and her body was brought to the Alejo County Morgue.

Toxicology: Positive for alprazolam.

Autopsy Results (Dictation by Dr. Fitch):

"The body of Ms. Bryson is notable for multiple lacerations, broad abrasions and multiple fractures of the limbs. The internal exam reflects severe injuries and blood is present in the thoracic cavities as well as the abdomen. Large lacerations are present to the liver and spleen. The mesentery is partially torn away from the abdominal wall and intestinal rupture is present at the cecum. There are multiple skull fractures.

Examination of the brain reveals subdural and subarachnoid hemorrhage due to blunt force head trauma. The brain surface is rinsed gently to reveal atrophy in the areas of the frontal lobe. The brain is sectioned and there is softening and necrosis in the area of the amygdala. Sections of the brain are examined under the microscope. Innumerable small round spaces are seen within the viable neurons of the amygdala but also in the frontal lobe of the brain. This confirms our worst fears."

Cause and Manner of Death:

Ms. Bryson demonstrated unusual behavior due to some undiagnosed underlying process that began just prior to her untimely death. She cut herself on a sharp rib edge of a patient that had an autopsy for an undiagnosed neurodegenerative disorder. It is now clear that the disorder was Type 2 infectious zombiism. Her autopsy examination revealed spongiform changes within brain tissue, in particular in the amygdala and frontal lobe, areas known to play roles in aggression and impulse control. This spongiform change is due to the Rapidly Infective Prion (RIP). But her immediate cause of death was actually due to the motor vehicle impact. In other words, the case would be signed out as "Blunt Force Traumatic Injuries due to Pedestrian-Vehicle Impact" and the manner of death would be an "Accident". Similar to Case 2, zombiism would have eventually caused her death but the accident was the immediate event that led to her death. The presence of zombiism would be listed as a contributing factor. Positive toxicology for alprazolam had no bearing on the case, as this is a common anti-anxiety medication that she had been prescribed.

Early Apocalypse Case 4: Ms. Chesterton Death at Home

Ms. Chesterton was a 63-year-old former schoolteacher that was found down in her home by her son Craig, who had journeyed to check on her when she didn't respond to phone calls. According to her son, she lived remotely in the country and had not shown up for a weekly Ladies of Orange County meeting that she never missed. He made the three-hour drive, forced his way into the home and found her deceased in the basement. She had many external injuries but the house was locked and there were no signs of forced entry. However, the house appeared like it was ransacked and there was abundant broken glass and furniture. The mail and newspapers were overflowing from her mailbox.

Toxicology: Negative.

Autopsy Results (Dictation by Dr. Fowzer)

"Ms. Chesterton's body is notable for numerous cuts, abrasions and contusions covering virtually every area of her body. She has fractures of the right radius, the left tibia and a completely dislocated left shoulder. The internal examination reveals an enlarged liver with fatty change, emphysematous changes of the lungs and hypertensive changes of the heart. The examination of the head reveals multiple contusions of the scalp. There is a small linear fracture of the right temporal bone. The skull is opened to reveal mild hemorrhage and severe atrophic changes of the frontal lobes of the brain with necrosis of the amygdala and frontal cortex. The microscopic examination of the brain reveals spongiform changes of virtually every area sampled."

Cause and Manner of Death:

The autopsy results are conclusive for Progressive Degenerative Disease of Aggression (Type 2 Zombiism) with the cause being a prion. Her injuries and the complete disarray of the home is evidence of disoriented and aggressive behavior. There was no one else in the home and the piled up mail and newspapers indicated that she had not left the home in days. The cause of death is "Progressive Degenerative Disease of Aggression (PDDA), Type 2 Zombiism" and the manner of death is natural. Infectious diseases such as PDDA are considered natural diseases. The only question that remains in this case is *how* she contracted the disease. It was never discovered.

Early Apocalypse Case 5: The Untimely Death of Mr. Evans

Mr. Evans was a 50-year-old male who was found dead in his home. There was a large amount of blood at the scene and the house appeared ransacked. Also of note was in this neighborhood, three other individuals were neutralized with the sickness that caused aggressive symptoms in many area patients. Examination of the scene reveals some high velocity blood spatter on walls and on the hardwood floor. The blood trail extends from the front door of the home into the bedroom hallway where Mr. Evans was found face down. Some blood was present on the front steps of the home. There were no signs of an accident, no broken glass and no other weapons present at the scene. Death investigators and police reported there were injuries to the neck. The body was taken to Wood Memorial County Morgue for autopsy.

Toxicology: Negative for substances.

Autopsy Results (Dictation by Dr. Jenkins)

"The body of Mr. Evans is noted to have injuries to the head and neck, forearms and hands. These injuries are incised wounds (cuts and stab wounds) and range from superficial to quite deep. Internal examination reveals that both the left internal jugular vein and the left common carotid artery are completely transected. The examination of the internal organs revealed mild atherosclerosis of the coronary arteries and mild fatty change of the liver. The brain appears normal grossly and there are no signs of atrophy. Given the urgency of the ongoing outbreak with an illness that appears to involve the brain, Mr. Evans' brain is sliced and sampled to look for areas of possible pathologic change. Examination of multiple sections of brain tissue under the microscope does not reveal any changes of prion diseases, inclusions (such as in rabies-like illnesses) or any other signs of infection or necrosis. It appears Mr. Evans bled out from his neck wounds."

Cause and Manner of Death:

The early part of the zombiism outbreak is evident from the case history. Violence has started to increase in which those affected with the disease are being neutralized, just as three had been in Mr. Evans neighborhood. Given that Mr. Evans was now dead from a violent injury, the question becomes did he have zombiism or not? His brain appeared to be perfectly normal both grossly (the unaided eye) and microscopically. This rules out infectious causes such as prion diseases, rabies-like virus and other infectious organisms. Thus, Mr. Evans cannot be diagnosed with the disease of zombiism. His cause of death is multiple stab wounds, with the wound to the left carotid and jugular vein causing him to bleed out and die (exsanguination). The manner of death is homicide. In this case, since Mr. Evans did not have zombiism, this appears to be a murder that may or may not be related to the ongoing outbreak. If society manages to survive the zombiism outbreak, this homicide would require investigation and murder charges.

Clinical and Pathological Correlation Case Studies

The Presenting Zombie Patient

The above histories are centered heavily on the experience of the pathologist. However, most cases will present to a health care practitioner early in the outbreak, just as unknowing doctors saw the early HIV patients before the disease had a name or a definitive causative agent. Undoubtedly, such cases would be perplexing to doctors and nurses and would result in confusion with other less lethal diseases; a health care provider cannot diagnose a disease that has never been described. So how would a clinic look early in a zombiism outbreak?

An isolated case or a handful of similar zombiism-like cases would not seem terribly unusual for an Emergency Physician or primary care doctor. It is not uncommon for a new or "bad" batch of drugs to hit the street and multiple psychotic patients end up at the clinic or ER. There would also likely be an influx of patients with wide ranging injuries.

Some would have the usual bruises, scratches and lacerations, but some who suffered a bite to the neck could have injured the carotid artery and would need immediate surgery to survive. The zombie patients would also likely be suffering some kind of injury either accidental or from someone who was defending themselves. Doctors and other medical professionals would need to be aware of the progression of symptoms for the bitten and injured. The rapid progression of severe psychiatric symptoms, pain, fever and finally loss of consciousness would be highly indicative of a possible zombiism infection. Such cases should trigger quarantine, but unfortunately most hospitals do not have a comprehensive zombiism program outlined in their patient protocols, despite the increased push for preparedness.

***

Case Study 1: Ms. Jones with Neck Pain

Clinic Note by Dr. Marucci, Family Practice, June 29

"Ms. Jones is a 25-year-old female who was in otherwise good condition until presenting this morning to the clinic with worrisome symptoms."

Chief Complaint:	Extreme sensitivity to light and "tightness and pain" in the neck muscles.	
Vital Signs:	Heart Rate:	119 beats per minute (normal: 60-100 bpm)
	Respiratory Rate:	20 breaths per minute (normal: 12-20 bpm)
	Blood Pressure:	155/94 (normal: 90/60 – 120/80)
	Temperature:	102° F / 38.9° C (normal: 98.6° F/37° C)

Physical Exam: Ms. Jones appears to be in distress and extremely fatigued. Her

eyes remain closed throughout the entire clinic visit. An attempt to examine her eyes to test pupillary light reflex was met with screams of pain and she knocked the penlight from my hand. She demonstrated severe hypersalivation to the point that she was constantly spitting saliva onto the exam table and floor. She failed an attempt to touch her chin to her chest and also had severe rigidity of the neck muscles. The heart sounds were normal and the lungs were clear. The abdominal exam revealed extreme sensitivity to touch. Examination of the extremities revealed an arc-shaped area of broken skin on the right wrist, which may be a human bite. The area appeared quite inflamed and was exquisitely sensitive to touch. Overall, she became somewhat combative during the physical examination and we decided on immediate hospital admission.

Preliminary Diagnosis: Suspected bacterial meningitis and an unusual injury to right wrist.

Treatment Plan: We will perform a lumbar puncture (spinal tap) and admit her to the hospital for intravenous broad-spectrum antibiotics to treat both the suspected meningitis and the possible infection of the wrist injury.

(Update June 30): Unfortunately, Ms. Jones did not respond to the antibiotic treatment and her condition worsened. She became extremely combative and attacked a group of medical students that were in the room on rounds. She was subsequently restrained and medical therapy for sedation and pain appeared ineffective. She was admitted to the ICU and developed severe cerebral edema, which did not respond to any medical therapy. Unfortunately, she did not survive her condition. The spinal tap did not show signs of bacterial meningitis and her blood cultures were negative. Because of this unusual condition in a previously healthy patient, we will order an autopsy to understand the cause of death."

Discussion & Autopsy Results

For a rabies-like virus (RLV) zombie agent, the patient may describe extreme sensitivity to light (photophobia), severe headache and possibly fever. The muscles may be tense throughout, particularly of the neck. Clinically, this could look very much like a case of acute meningitis, an infection of the brain's linings. Like meningitis, the patient may have altered consciousness but with the addition of the excess saliva commonly seen in rabies infections.

Ultimately, the process in the brain involved inflammatory changes that caused cerebral edema (brain swelling) and death. The reason why brain swelling is so dangerous and must be dealt with swiftly is that the skull cannot expand. This forces the soft brain tissue through the path of least resistance in the skull, which is the foramen magnum. The foramen magnum is the quarter-sized hole in the base of the skull where the brainstem transitions to the spinal cord. Death occurs because pressure is exerted on the areas of the brainstem that control breathing and heartbeat. The results of this autopsy exam confirmed the presence of rabies or a rabies-like viral (RLV) infection, including inclusion bodies within Purkinje cells of the cerebellum.

Case 2: Mr. Dawson's Rapid Decline

Clinic Note by Dr. Wycoff, Internal Medicine, December 18

"Mr. Dawson is a 30-year-old male that presents to the clinic with confusion and erratic behavior.

Chief Complaint: The patient cannot articulate speech. His roommate Ms. Drake, who gives the history of his illness, brought him to the clinic. Mr. Dawson is reported to have developed confusion during a night on the town. His friends thought this was due to possible intoxication or food poisoning. The next morning, Mr. Dawson was found staring into space and did not respond to commands. Ms. Drake became concerned and brought him to the clinic. She completely denies that they ingested any kind of illicit substances.

Vital Signs: Heart Rate: 88 beats per minute (normal: 60-100 bpm)

Respiratory Rate: 11 breaths per minute (normal: 12-20 bpm)

Blood Pressure: 123/79 (normal: 90/60 – 120/80)

Temperature: 97.1° F / 36.1° C (normal: 98.6° F/37° C)

Physical Exam: Mr. Dawson appears catatonic. His mouth is agape. His skin feels cool. The heart and lungs sound normal and there is no pain on abdominal exam. There are no bites or injuries to the body. He has decreased reflexes but was otherwise normal. He did not respond to commands that I gave him, but as the exam continued he appeared to get more irritable. Within about 10 minutes of start of the exam he refused to allow me to touch him. Without being able to examine him, I began to prepare his referral to a neurologist, and without warning he leapt off the table and attempted to attack his friend in the room. Security was called and it took two nurses, myself and two guards to subdue him. Unfortunately, security guard was bitten during the incident but refused medical treatment.

Preliminary Diagnosis: Unspecified poisoning and excited delirium; possibly drug intoxication.

Treatment Plan: Mr. Dawson was restrained, urgently sent to the ER for a psychiatric and neurological consultation. We will perform a lumbar puncture (spinal tap), a drug screen and a head CT scan to look for intracranial lesions."

(Update Dec 20): "Mr. Dawson's condition continued to worsen. The drug screen was negative. The head CT scan revealed some atrophy changes in the frontal lobe. This is an unusual result for someone only 30 years old. The lumbar puncture results came back positive for the 14-3-3 protein. This confirms that Mr. Dawson almost certainly has a prion-based disease of the brain. He is under maximal sedation and we have spoken to the family with regards to hospice care. There is no recovery for prion-based diseases. Upon his expiration, we will order an autopsy to better characterize the disease."

Discussion & Autopsy

The presentation of the rapid loss of mental function is unlike typical prion diseases. These diseases tend to take years for incubation and then months for the symptoms to worsen. The presence of 14-3-3 protein in a lumbar puncture is strong evidence that a prion disease is present. The CT scan showing atrophy of the frontal lobes is a common finding for dementia-related changes. Given that altered mental status occurred almost overnight, this is suggestive of the Rapidly Infective Prion (RIP). It should be noted that Mr. Dawson's decreased reflexes and decreased body temperature suggests a possible pseudo-hibernation state that patients with the RIP might manifest.

Overall, his symptoms continued to progress quickly as he went from a catatonic phase to aggression in just mere hours. This case illustrates why it is important to restrain all patients that are suspected of having a zombiism infection; it is likely the bitten security guard will also become a Type 2 zombie. The autopsy examination revealed atrophy of the brain and sections of the tissue revealed the classic spongiform changes seen within neurons throughout the brain.

These cases should merely be considered instructive examples. A patient presenting in the prodromal phase of zombiism will be a diagnostic challenge. Complicating matters is that virtually no medical schools have Zombiology sections in their 2nd year pathology courses or during clinical medicine clerkships. As such, few health care professionals have appropriate training to recognize zombiism in the clinical setting.

Cases During Epidemic or Pandemic Phase Zombiism

Once local, state and federal health departments realize there is a zombiism crisis, the information will be rapidly disseminated. In the case of the Bath Salts "Zombie" in Miami, it made national and worldwide news within 24 hours. It is likely that before the Bath Salts "Zombie" autopsy was completed, hundreds of millions of people already knew about the case because of the media exposure.

During zombiism's early phase, there will likely not be any major changes to diagnostic or security protocols. But as the disease is reported in multiple geographic areas and in increasing numbers of individuals, it will be clear that there is an epidemic. Once epidemic phase is reached, it will change the way these patients are handled. In the Pre-Apocalyptic phase, the above case studies reflected physicians and patients that were unaware of the possible zombiism diagnosis. Unfortunately, this is when the disease will spread the fastest. As zombiism begins to pick up steam at clinics and Emergency Departments, it won't take long for these unusual incidents to be reported, even if the cause is completely unknown. If the zombiism diagnosis is definitely known, it will be mandatory that universal precautions be used at all times during patient contact. Protective eyewear (goggles or face shield) and full protective gown and gloves would need to be worn at all times. Because the nature of the illness would be uncertain, all personnel would have to wear N-95 masks, a special type of mask that prevents the spread of tuberculosis and other respiratory illnesses. A maximum amount of cover-up would be ideal, in particular for areas that could be bitten such as the hands and arms. Because those in an excited delirium or hyperaggressive state can have almost superhuman strength, restraints might have to be secured and sedation increased. The following case studies give examples of how pre-epidemic zombiism patients might present to a health care provider.

Case 3: Ms. Barin's Death During Attack

Chart Note by Dr. Buchalski, Emergency Physician, November 9

"Ms. Barin is a 30-year-old female that was brought to the Emergency Department after attempting to attack a neighbor. She suffered a blunt force injury to the head as the homeowner defended herself with a baseball bat.

Chief Complaint: Ms. Barin is unconscious but is presumed to be suffering from the affliction of zombiism, as has occurred in at least 50 other patients over the past two weeks. She is received in the ED, restrained by paramedics and heavily sedated.

Vital Signs: Heart Rate: 188 beats per minute (normal: 60-100 bpm)

Respiratory Rate: 32 breaths per minute (normal: 12-20 bpm)

Blood Pressure: 210/105 (normal: 90/60 – 120/80)

Temperature: 106° F / 41.1° C (normal: 98.6° F/37° C)

Physical Exam: Ms. Barin is unconscious and restrained. The physical exam is limited. She is covered head to toe with sweat. The heart and lungs sound normal but she shakes violently when touched. She did not respond to commands.

There are no bites to the body. There is a large laceration of the forehead, approximately 10 centimeters in maximal dimension. Her clothes are blood-soaked and the wound is still bleeding. A resident physician (Dr. McKenzie) was exposed, as the patient spat blood and saliva onto her face. Dr. McKenzie was not wearing goggles or a mask.

Preliminary Diagnosis: Type 2 Zombiism, Infectious Type

Treatment Plan: Ms. Barin was restrained and additional sedative medications were given. We will defer the lumbar puncture because based on CDC reports, virtually all individuals tested have the prion zombiism, referred to as the Rapidly Infective Prion (RIP). A head CT will be performed to assess for brain injury but otherwise the patient will be admitted to the hospice unit after the head wound is sutured closed."

Discussion

During the full-blown epidemic phase, there would be awareness that the disease is both highly communicable and fatal. As a result, not much time would be spent on confirming the disease diagnosis; there is currently no rapid test for prion disease and it would be difficult to develop one in short order during an apocalyptic outbreak. Doctors would be able to recognize the disease on sight and from the scene descriptions. In this case, Ms. Barin attempted to attack a neighbor, and was injured in a defensive response. When she was brought in, she had hyperthermia and extremely high heart rate, breathing and blood pressure. A CT scan was ordered to assess for any possible treatable medical or surgical conditions. Whether viral or prion, it is highly unlikely that the disease would be treatable. Thus these patients would be taken to either established or makeshift hospice units. The disposition of patients with terminal zombiism would produce many legal and ethical dilemmas regarding end of life care.

There is no established biological basis for Type 1 zombiism (Resurrected Dead). However, because of the remote possibility of the dead walking and the persistence of the classic zombie characteristics in the public mind, we present a case study.

Case 4: Mr. Garroway

Clinic Note by Dr. Martinez, Family Practice, October 13

"Mr. Garroway is a 33-year-old male that is brought to the clinic by his live in girlfriend, Nicole.

Chief Complaint: The patient cannot speak for himself but he does moan. Nicole states that he 'doesn't seem himself', 'smells bad' and is "totally being weird".

Vital Signs: Heart Rate: 0 beats per minute (normal: 60-100 bpm)

                      Respiratory Rate: 0 breaths per minute (normal: 12-20 bpm)

                      Blood Pressure: 0/0 (normal: 90/60 – 120/80)

                      Temperature: 78° F / 25.6° C (normal: 98.6° F/37° C)

Physical Exam: Mr. Garroway appears ill. His skin is pale gray to light green. A foul odor emanates from him. His skin feels cool and many areas of skin appear to have sloughed off. He does not respond to any questions but his mouth is agape and he moans loudly on occasion. There is no heartbeat or breath sounds. He does not respond to sensation and his neurological exam is absent of muscle reflexes and cranial nerve functions. On attempting to walk, there is obvious unsteadiness of gait. There are no injuries to the body. A few areas that look like particulate matter or saw dust are present around the eyes and in the mouth. On close inspection these appear to be moving and are fly eggs.

Preliminary Diagnosis: Type 1 Zombiism.

<u>Treatment Plan:</u>   Mr. Garroway was admitted to the Type 1 zombiism hospice unit

at North Memorial Hospital. He will remain in quarantine until we receive further

instructions on what to do with this influx of walking corpses. No tests are ordered

because the patient is decomposing and no fluids are left in the body. Radiology scans

would be of little value, as the patient appears to be the same as the others in the

outbreak: Dead.

(Update Oct 31): Mr. Garroway's condition continued to worsen. Maggots developed and

much of his face and torso is defleshed. Decomposition progressed and the bloating phase

has passed. The skin now appears dark green to black. As there is no treatment, Mr.

Garroway will continue to decompose until the second death is reached. At that point, the

remains will be sent to the Pathologist, Dr. Arwa."

<u>Discussion</u>

Type 1 zombiism is undoubtedly a terminal condition due to the progression of the

natural forces of decomposition. In a clinical setting in which the corpse is protected from

the elements, the entire process from presentation to complete decay would take weeks to

months. Since the Type 1 zombie cannot be killed (because it is already dead), the

question is: Should we allow nature to take its course in a controlled setting or hasten the

process with a neutralization technique involving the head? These are difficult questions

that would be for the family and the legal system to decide.

<u>Is Zombicide the Same as Homicide?</u>

One way that humankind distinguishes itself from the animal world is through the

creation of laws for an orderly and self-governed society. The forensic pathologist is a

central part in determining whether or not a criminal death has occurred. Certainly the early focus for the forensic pathologist would be to perform autopsies on all cases that appear to be homicides. A homicide is defined as *the deliberate unlawful killing of one person by another person.* One of the biggest questions during a zombie outbreak is whether or not a dead body was intentionally killed. This could have legal implications should society survive and the legal structure of the country remain intact. Unlawful killings, even of zombies, would need to be investigated. So would **zombicide**—the "killing" of a zombie—hold the same moral weight or legal implications as killing an unaffected human?

A zombie legal expert of the law firm Kuun, Ambrozi, Cole and Riddle commented on the matter:

"In the apocalyptic phase of an outbreak, we would hope that the killing/neutralization of a zombie would fall under the heading of 'justifiable homicide', but would it? Zombiism cases would be unique in our legal system, but we must also look at precedent. Remember that a Type 2 zombie is still a living human. In the case of the Bath Salts "Zombie" and other excited delirium cases that were terminated by lethal force, the manner of death is almost always ruled a 'Homicide', but it would not have been murder that we would bring criminal charges for because due to the threat to human life, the actions of officers or armed citizens were lawful and justifiable."

In other words, if society were to survive the apocalypse there will still be consequences for our actions, despite the pop culture depictions of the immediate dissolution of law. It is understandable that part of the appeal of post-apocalyptic or dystopian fantasy is to live in a world where citizens make their own rules. At one time or another, we have all imagined what it would be like if laws did not exist. But there are many moral and ethical dilemmas that surround the zombie apocalypse, and deep philosophical questions would be raised in such a pandemic. While thought experiments on the matter can be helpful, it is the reality of such an outbreak that will force us to answer these questions in real time.

***

Early in a zombiism outbreak, the autopsy will play a central role in elucidating the underlying cause of disease. Like many new diseases, discovery will rely on a multidisciplinary approach involving all fields of medicine and epidemiology. Such a concerted effort may be the only hope to stall the disease at the 'local outbreak' stage and prevent its expansion to a full-blown pandemic. The above case studies are hypothetical examples that are constructed based on how similar disease conditions may present. It should be understood that despite our best preparation and our extensive body of medical knowledge, the eventual zombiism outbreak might present in ways we have never seen and could not have predicted.

PART V:

Why Humans Will (Probably) Survive the Zombie Apocalypse

"This is not a test of the Emergency Broadcast System. Repeat: This is not a test. Hordes of extremely aggressive zombie-like individuals are sweeping this region. The counties of Orange, Washington, Crawford, Lawrence and Jackson are currently affected. Take shelter immediately. Secure all doors and windows. Do not attempt to leave your home until local Health Department or Law Enforcement officials have confirmed that the area has been secured. Remain on standby until further notice."

Imagine getting a notification like this on your smartphone, TV or radio. How would you respond? Immediately update Twitter? Do a Snapchat story with a zombie filter? Hopefully you would grab as many supplies as possible, arm yourself and settle in your home until it's over. As it turns out, few families have a comprehensive Zombie Preparedness Plan. The following sections will break down the threat level of both the Type 1 and Type 2 apocalypses in terms of mathematics and the physical variables that will govern the zombies. Fortunately, the odds are much in the favor of the living and uninfected, but survival will require adequate preparation, education and patience.

The Type I Apocalypse: Surviving the Resurrected Dead

The Resurrected Dead represent the classic 'End Days' scenario: Hordes of rotting zombies emerging from graves, mausoleums, funeral homes and hospital morgues to attack (and possibly eat) the living. But how much of a threat are these Type 1 zombies? Do the living have any chance of withstanding this macabre threat? Our assessment is that a Type 1 apocalypse will be a manageable and quite possibly an easily survivable threat if the appropriate steps are taken.

To understand the scope of the Type 1 apocalypse, the plague must be broken down on two fronts: 1) the physical variables that govern zombie survival 2) the mathematics and sheer numbers of zombies that the living would face. What we must remember is that Type 1 zombies are subject to the forces of decomposition, and thus will have to face many physical variables that will diminish their threat. This has been problematic for zombiologists, particularly those that ascribe to supernatural Type I zombies. This discordance has given rise to the Zombie Paradox.

The Zombie Paradox & Mythbusting: Type 1 Zombies

The dead rising from the grave goes against what is scientifically known about the nature of life and death and thus falls under the realm of a supernatural or metaphysical force. If one accepts that zombies are supernatural then they cannot be explained within the laws of physics and chemistry. And yet we live in a world with well-defined and inescapable scientific laws, so if zombies emerge how can they be supernatural? This is the Zombie Paradox, and applies only to the classical form of zombies (Type I). The Paradox causes us to have to reconsider some of the long-held beliefs about zombies and put them to rest. We examine the limitations of the Type 1 zombie in terms of the anatomical and physiological variables that differentially affect the walking corpses instead of the living. The extent of the attack waged by the resurrected dead will be mild in comparison to what is seen in pop culture. But we must free ourselves from these long held myths about zombies if we are to face the apocalypse in a scientific and logical manner. Doing so may promote our survival.

Zombie Senses: Will They Be Able to Find You?

Like any human or animal, we respond to external stimuli with our senses. Will zombies find us if we are hiding or trying to get away? Judging by all examples of zombies in pop culture, they *know* how to find us. A barking dog, a light left on after dark or the smoke from a burning fire could tip off a zombie horde to your location. Yet, how can a zombie hear, see and smell despite the presence of decay?

Generally speaking, sensation involves a multistep process that occurs in a fraction of a second. Our bodies have sense organs that respond to stimuli such as an image, a touch or a sound. The stimulus is conducted to the brain via nerves connected to that sense organ, and in the brain the sensory stimulus is processed, allowing us to interpret what we have sensed. This would be difficult for the zombie.

For hearing, the external ear would be reasonably intact due its cartilage composition. The eardrum (tympanic membrane), the ear canal and the bones of the middle ear would all remain intact. The issue would be with nerve conduction, particularly as the nerve decays along with the brain itself. In normal humans, hearing occurs by way of cranial nerve 8 (vestibulocochlear nerve, CN VIII) and the various related centers of the brain that allow a person to respond to sounds. The brain begins to liquefy after several days, but prior to this breakdown process the machinery for hearing would be intact. The detection of sound waves would diminish as the decay progresses.

Vision might be the most problematic of all the zombie senses. After death there is no longer the production of tears to lubricate the eye, which is likely what gives rise to the gray-white cloudiness of the front of the eyes. Even in non-zombie corpses, the corneas can become clouded just a few hours after death, although this is highly variable. The decay of the inner part of the eye makes the efficacy of zombie attacks even less likely. The retina is a very delicate layer of cells at the back of the eye that contains the rods and cones that allow us to see. But shortly after death, the retina begins to degenerate and detach from the back of the eye, thus completely inhibiting the projection of an image for the brain to interpret. Although the optic nerves (cranial nerve 2, CNII) are sturdy structures about the diameter of a phone charging cord, the higher functions of visual translation in the brain would only be as good as the integrity of the brain itself. Zombies would have great visual difficulties as decay progressed.

At most, zombies would only respond to broad, quick movements and to generalities of light and dark. To imagine what zombie vision might be like, try looking through a panel of frosted glass. Such poor sight would present bigger problems than ineffective visual tracking of human prey. Without excellent vision, zombies would have many unintended falls and injuries, thereby weakening their attacks and their numbers. Even the clear-eyed zombies without cataracts or clouded corneas would have extremely poor vision, certainly well past the point of legal blindness.

Like hearing and vision, the sense of smell would certainly be dulled. The olfactory nerve (cranial nerve 1, CNI) is a large nerve near the front of the brain and receives smell input from nerves in the nose. It is extremely doubtful that smell would be acute enough to home in on a particular scent, such as the scent of living humans or of smoke from a fire. It is reasonable to hypothesize that hearing would be the sense most intact for zombies, because nearly the entire sense apparatus would remain intact prior to liquefaction of the brain. Regardless, it is wise to err on the side of caution and assume that all zombies have intact and acute sensation.

Zombie Movement: Will They Catch You?

When it comes to zombie movement there are two drastically different renditions. The most common is the lumbering and uncoordinated movement of the *Walking Dead* type zombies. These zombies do not overwhelm in strength but attain their effect from the sheer numbers of persistent corpses. Other zombies have been shown to be as fast and as athletic as an unaffected human. But what is the reality of the situation?

For the Resurrected Dead, the concept of speed and agility is a nonstarter. Coordinated physical speed requires muscular strength, intact tendons and ligaments and good nerve conduction. In addition, higher brain functions must be intact to initiate the movements. At the moment of death, cellular physiology changes from its active, specialized purpose to breakdown and decomposition. Thus, long dead corpses or those with extensive decomposition would have decreased (or absent) muscle mass, degenerated tendons and ligaments and nerve conduction would be impossible. Thus, the Resurrected Dead should be quite slow if they are under control of the physical properties of the known and visible universe. Embalmed corpses would be just as ineffective due to the chemical restriction of muscular movement by embalming fixatives.

The freshly dead have a better prospect. These are dead bodies that have not yet undergone the process of decomposition. Even despite the process of autolysis and breakdown, the muscle mass would be equivalent to what it would was during life. Ligaments and tendons would be in perfect condition. Consider that ligaments and tendons from cadavers are used every day by orthopedic surgeons around the world to repair torn and ruptured ones in the living.

Finally, although nerve conduction would be very poor in the freshly dead, the nerves themselves would be intact. Think of this as a power cord plugged in, but electricity to the outlet is interrupted. Restoring electricity to this outlet will allow the cord to have power.[11] The biggest issue would be that of the brain tissue. In decomposing corpses, the brain tissue may be almost completely liquefied. The brain no longer possesses its familiar appearance of undulating grooves of gray matter, but rather has no form and is the consistency of a thick soup. But in the freshly dead, the brain may retain its usual appearance for days if the body is refrigerated shortly after death.

Despite common beliefs, non-zombie corpses do not move of their own volition. We've all heard that corpses might suddenly sit up, flinch or move in some way after death. This is false. Before rigor mortis sets in and after it dissipates, the body has no muscular tone to produce movement. During the stiffening process of rigor mortis, if one attempts to adjust the arms or fingers of the corpse, it will often resist manipulation and even snap back into place, giving the appearance of autonomous movement. But this is not a

---

[11] This was the goal of Dr. Frankenstein's work.

conscious process or even a reflex; it is merely a physical property of stiff muscles and joints.

Zombie Motive: Will They Eat You?

"Braaaaaains!!"

The notion of brain-eating zombies was not a core feature of any zombie—real or fictional—all the way up through 1985. In that year, the movie *Return of the Living Dead* was released and featured zombies that not only craved brains, but also *spoke* the desire to eat brains. This is where the famous "Braaaains!" phrase originates. Since then, the brain-craving trait has been amplified as a mainstay in the lore of pop culture zombies. But there are numerous logical problems with the brain-craving motive.

If hunger is part of the zombie attack motive, it is more likely that the zombie's instincts—which are the same as our primal instincts—would first lead them to search for food that is easy to obtain. It is a basic survival instinct that a fully functional human or animal will take the easy meal over the difficult to obtain food. For someone affected with zombiism it would be much more time and energy efficient to find and eat a Twinkie than it would be to try and get inside of a human head. The reason for this is primarily anatomical.

The very fact that are skulls are so thick and so hard is a gift of evolution that has allowed us to survive as a species to present day. Because the brain is the control center for every human function, it must be protected. If human ancestors from millions of years ago had thin skull bones, there would have been countless fatal brain injuries due to relatively minor trauma. Moreover, non-fatal brain injuries could have affected movement or senses such as vision or hearing, all of which would have been essential for hunting or defense from animals or other attackers. A thin skull would have been a negative survival trait. In other words, if you die easily from minor trauma, then you won't live long enough to reproduce. If you cannot reproduce then you will go extinct. Hard headedness is a gift. One does not need a medical degree to arrive at this conclusion. Yet, despite getting into medical school I still accepted the dogma that zombies ate brains. That is, until I personally had to open a human head during autopsy.

The basic anatomy of the head makes it very difficult to get into skull without the use of tools or vicious blunt force. To open the head during an autopsy, the scalpel must pass through the thick scalp skin and layer of subcutaneous fat that cushions the skull. In an average human scalp this is about 1 to 2 centimeters in thickness, or about the width of a thumbnail. In addition, there are band-like muscles of the head, most prominent of which are the temporalis muscles on the sides of the head just above the ears. The temporalis muscles (which are used for moving the lower jaw) in particular can be quite thick. The forensic pathologist or autopsy technician must then loosen up all of this tissue by placing the fingers between the skull bone and the scalp tissue and dissecting it free. Even with excellent technique this process often takes at least 5 minutes and can take much longer if the scalp is thick or there is a mess of hair. A zombie would only be able to use hands and teeth to rip through hair, scalp tissue and possibly the temporalis muscles just to get to the surface of the bony skull.

Even if this time- and energy-consuming process is achieved, the skull bone (calvarium) must be broken open to get access to the brain. Again, we return to our autopsy example for the best-case scenario of getting a head open. During autopsy, the skull is opened with an electric bone saw, which is a special type of saw that features a round blade with numerous small teeth at its edge. Rather than cutting straight through the bone in the way that a chainsaw cuts through wood, the saw blade oscillates at a high frequency, grinding through the bone due to friction and pressure. A well-executed bone saw cut on a skull by a skilled autopsy practitioner might take around five minutes. Once the cut is completed, a T-shaped tool known as a "skull key" is placed into the cleft produced by the saw and given a firm twist, causing the top of the skull to pop open and expose the brain. In the most skilled hands that are equipped with a full set of tools, the entire process of brain access takes about 10 minutes.

Back to our 'struggling zombie' example, how does the creature manage to get into the skull without tools? The skull bone approaches or exceeds 1 centimeter (a little less than half an inch) in thickness with the exception of two areas: the anterior portion of the temporal bone and the eye socket. Even in these areas (which are more extensively profiled in Part III of the text) we have seen attempted stab wounds to the skull in both these areas that did not break the bone or enter into the skull.

If in fact there is a "hunger" or "craving" motive of the zombie, it is very likely based on the acute need for energy in order to stay "alive". While brains are highly nutritious, they are a completely impractical food source because of the difficulty in getting them out of the skull. You can consider your brains completely safe from zombie attack.

Bite Transmission: Will I Become One of Them?

It is considered accepted and irrefutable dogma that zombies must pass the infection with a bite. While this is a truly terrifying and painful method, there are many problems with bite transmission. If the apocalypse consists of Type 1, resurrected zombies, the threat of bite transmission is low and will decrease with time since death. The teeth in a corpse are often very loose due to decomposition. The decay of the gingiva and the lost integrity of dental ligaments that hold teeth in place would result in a "One Bite Zombie". A bite onto flesh would likely cause the extraction of multiple teeth and thus render useless further attacking power of this zombie. This would limit the spread of the disease because only one zombie could create one zombie, not multiple zombies. Moreover, zombies that were already edentulous (without teeth) due to advanced age or early tooth decay (such as Meth Zombies) would be ineffective at biting from the outset. In general, biting is an ineffective way to spread a disease because it requires such close contact and skin breakage. This is much more difficult to achieve than passing a disease simply by sneezing or coughing.

Type 1 Zombies: Apocalyptic Mathematics

The dead far outnumber the living but exactly how many of these walking dead would we have to face when the time comes? There are two very different groups of Type 1 zombies: The Buried Dead and the Freshly Dead. Each group is governed by different physical and environmental factors and the numerical challenges of the zombies are vastly different. While the Buried Dead are a fixed number, the numbers of Freshly Dead would simply depend on the numbers of people dying and converting and would thus increase over time.

The Buried Dead (BD)

The resurrection of the dead is undoubtedly a supernatural event, but will it be truly apocalyptic? This depends on what one means by apocalyptic. These days we use the term in a general fashion to describe any kind of cataclysm such as an earth-asteroid impact, a global famine or a humanity-destroying infection. But the word actually has its roots in very specific theology. The word 'apocalypse' is derived from two Greek words that together become *apokaluptein*. The translation of the word means 'to uncover or reveal' and is in direct reference to the Book of Revelation.

In the Christian understanding, the apocalypse is the complete and final destruction of the world and the *revealing* of the kingdom of God during the last stage of the Christian saga. Scripture aside, the interpretation of beliefs surrounding this event actually play a role in how many intact bodies we might have to face when the time comes. It seems every Christian sect has a different take on how apocalyptic revelation will manifest. No matter who is right or wrong, it is the burial and mortuary practices in the West that are the primary determinant for just how many zombies we will face and in what condition they will be in. One aim of modern funeral practice is to preserve the body for its final moments on this physical Earth, after resurrection.

Many "Rapture theorists" teach that reanimated corpses will rise from the grave but will not attack the living. Instead, "saved souls" will simply float off into the sky to meet God, who will appear in the East. This is why most graves face east in the countries where Christianity is the predominant religion. But because the scripture speaks of the *physical* body rising from the grave, good preservation of the corpse became important so that it would be intact at the time of the final resurrection. It is this preservation process that results in a much higher number of potential zombies (Z_p) than if the physical body was thought to be unnecessary for this moment.

To preserve the body, morticians use embalming fluid that contains preservatives, including the chemical formaldehyde (CH_2O). Formaldehyde acts to stabilize the tissues and prevent decay by cross-linking proteins and deactivating enzymes that normally degrade cells. This was desirable when loved ones had to travel long distances to a funeral or if the body had to be transported a great distance. In fact, the practice of embalming came into wide use during the time of the American Civil War (1860-1865). It was quite common for a man to die on the battlefield hundreds of miles from his home and it would take days to transport the body. Before the advent of embalming, the body would have undergone the process of decomposition on the expected timeline of a few days after death.

The embalming process works so well that if the coffin remains intact, corpses exhumed after decades can look virtually the same as when they were buried. But it is excellent preservation that so dramatically limits the corpse should it resurrect. The work of the mortician is well appreciated when examining exhumed bodies. But the body is often heavily damaged in cases where the coffin was breached with ground water and soil. The effect of cold temperatures and moisture can change the flesh to a mass of what is known as adipocere. **Adipocere** is a kind of dense fatty substance that turns the flesh to the consistency of rubber. A human body becomes virtually unrecognizable, looking more like an ash-covered body from the ruins of Pompeii than a person. There may also be fungal growth, which can also thrive in cool, damp environments. When one considers the number of burials throughout history that were not embalmed or those that were buried in faulty coffins, it's easy to see why a large percentage of these corpses would be a limited attacking threat. But despite limitations, the sheer numbers of potential resurrected dead (Z_p) Type I zombies seem to have a dramatic theoretical advantage. Our starting point for calculation is the emergence of anatomically modern humans around 50,000 years ago. Since that time, it is estimated that approximately 100 billion people have lived and died before modern day. This gives us 100 billion Z_p versus approximately 7 billion currently living humans, a theoretical mismatch of 14 Type 1 zombies per 1 living human. Those are not good odds, even with the living population having higher cognition and being well armed. But it appears to get even worse for the living.

Of the 7 billion people currently on Earth, not everyone is capable of taking on the zombie hordes. Approximately 2 billion are children and another 2 billion are elderly, a total of 4 billion individuals. This changes the Z_p /Living ratio to 33 zombies per 1 living human. If one factors in disability and chronic diseases of those 3 billion living, this might involve another billion individuals, leaving approximately 2 billion humans to take on the zombies, a ratio that approaches 50 Z_p to 1 Living. Even though survival prospects seem bleak, the Z_p numbers are grossly misleading. An examination of the factors that might inhibit the Type 1 zombie hordes reveals a much fairer fight.

Starting with the 100 billion Z_p, a significant number are the "unpreserved dead", defined as all deaths from around 50,000 years ago to around 160 years ago. Because most of these corpses were buried, entombed or ceremonially destroyed, the unpreserved dead will not play a significant role in any zombie apocalypse. At best, these ancient bodies would be reduced to mere skeletons, which are the weakest and least threatening of resurrected dead. The actual zombie (Z_A, also called "Zombie Actual") numbers would arise almost totally from those that have died in the last 160 years.

Since the time of the Civil War (1860s), a large percentage of these individuals were embalmed. Using the time frame of 1860 to present day, approximately 3 billion individuals have died, resulting in a Z_p of 3 billion. This results in a ratio close to 1 zombie per 1 (effective) living individual, a fair numerical fight. But how much of a threat would such a corpse be?

Physical Variables of Burial

The issue of encasement is the primary determinant for why the resurrected dead will *not* 'rise from the grave'. The late part of the 19th century and early part of the 20th century had millions of burials in weakly reinforced caskets such as the classic pine boxes. These bodies would have undoubtedly experienced extensive decomposition to the point of rendering the corpse a zero threat, similar to any body buried in the ground since antiquity. But in the last half of the 20th century most bodies were buried in coffins meant to resist environmental conditions and to keep the body intact. Regardless of the number of corpses buried since the mid-20th century, the reanimated corpses would face a near impossibility in attempting to escape their coffins. Rising from the grave will be much more difficult than it sounds.

The average grave plot is 8 feet long, 3 feet wide and a coffin at the bottom would have 6 feet of soil on top of it; this would result in a grave plot soil volume totaling 144 cubic feet (8 x 3 x 6 ft). Given that 1 cubic foot of dry soil weighs about 40 pounds, this results in a pressure on top of the coffin of 5,760 pounds (144 cubic feet of soil x 40 pounds per cubic foot). In other words, the already-weakened corpse would have to escape the coffin then overcome nearly three tons of soil pressure to make it to the surface. If the soil was saturated with water the pressure would be even greater.

Making the situation even worse, many of the Type 1 zombies would have had severe injuries or end stage illnesses that had caused their deaths. This would markedly limit their attacking power. Still others would have been cremated, an increasing trend in the last 30 years. As a matter of completeness, our group has received many questions about the fate of cremated remains during a resurrection of the dead. While it seems rather obvious, the dust and minute charred bone fragments (referred to as '**cremains**') are not expected to reanimate in the absence of a true metaphysical miracle.

Overall the effective Z_p of the buried dead is far less than one zombie per living human. The odds of the buried dead and the ancient dead forming a meaningful resurrection to society are virtually zero, although archaeologists might have some surprises while on digs. A graveyard-style resurrection would be so ineffective that it might have already happened and we haven't even noticed because all the corpses are trapped underground or in tombs.

The Freshly Dead (FD)

There is a Type 1 zombie threat that is far more significant than the Buried Dead. The Freshly Dead are defined as bodies that have ceased all neurological and physiologic activity ("clinical death"), but have reanimated prior to the mortuary, autopsy or burial processes.

The Freshly Dead include:

- Bodies that have not yet been taken to the morgue (hospital deaths)
- Bodies that are in the morgue
- Bodies in funeral homes prior to burial
- Bodies that have died indoors or outdoors but have not yet been discovered

For this section we only focus on the country where our research group is located: The United States of America. Each country would have to refer to their own death statistics for an assessment of their national threat. In the USA, just shy of 8,000 people die every day. This translates to about 8,000 Z_p available for reanimation per day. Given the Buried

Dead zombie numbers that were in the billions, this seems a highly manageable threat. Of

the 8,000 Z_p, a large number of those deaths would be elderly patients who were expected

to die from natural processes such as old age, chronic diseases or terminal illness.

Another portion of the Freshly Dead would consist of premature infants and children. Yet

another group would involve those who perished in accidents or other violent deaths with

severe bodily injuries; decapitation or dismemberment would greatly limit the attacking

power of the potential zombie corpse. Thus, many fewer than 8,000 corpses would

produce a significant threat, perhaps in the range of 4,000 freshly dead per day. To

understand the scale of this daily threat, a small to medium sized town might not have a

single person die for weeks.

However, if the corpses continue to reanimate, the threat will grow by 8,000 new

zombies each day. For perspective, 30 days of persistent resurrection would result in

240,000 new zombies. In 6 months of resurrection, 1.44 million zombies. In one year,

there would be 2.92 million zombies. This of course ignores the likely persistent

neutralization of the zombies by citizens and law enforcement. Given that we do not

know how effective such a zombie neutralization campaign would be, we do not attempt

to estimate the effect it would have on the overall zombie number. The population of the

USA is over 320 million, but when one excludes children, the elderly and the chronically

ill, perhaps 150 million individuals are able to take up the fight against the zombies.

These 150 million adults (with 300 million guns) would retain a hefty advantage.

From a purely theoretical standpoint, a continued baseline death rate of 8,000 per day

would take 12,500 days for all functional adult humans to die and be converted to zombies. In other words, the point at which potential zombies Z_p = Zombie Actual Z_A is 34.2 years. To reach the midway point, in which the number of walking dead equals the number of living, this would be 17.1 years.

Fictional accounts suggest a nearly 'instant apocalypse' in which society is wiped out in a month or less. This is really only a possibility if the zombie plague was communicable from the dead to the living, which would cause many more individuals to be affected than was calculated (changing both the Z_p and Z_A), and the timeline would be shortened. Given that dead tissue cannot support living infectious organisms this is unlikely. The only infectious agent that would make sense is the prion, because it does not require living tissue to exist. In fact, no amount of bleach, alcohol or usual sterilization procedures can destroy it.

Numerical advantages aside, the destabilizing effect of a risen dead apocalypse would be profound. All facets of life, school, work, the economy, and religious and political institutions would be profoundly affected both domestically and abroad. It is likely that the chaotic decisions of the living could be more damaging to society that any deleterious effects of the dead. Thus we urge an approach to surviving the apocalypse based in patience and inertia in which the natural process of decomposition is allowed to progress. Based on these principles, our group created the Run, Hide, Wait™ Strategy which will decrease chaos and maximize the chances of survival.

The RUN, HIDE, WAIT™ Strategy

In studying best practices for apocalyptic survival, our group created many algorithms and computer models to assess for the lethality of the apocalypse. As it turns out, winning against the Dead should be relatively easy. But our recommended strategy is in stark contrast to virtually all the depictions of apocalyptic survival in zombie fiction. Of those surveyed, only 6% of respondents have a well-formulated Zombie Preparedness Plan. Most of these plans focused on the advice of commercially available survival guides or what they had seen in movies or TV. Many such plans focus too heavily on weapons and long apocalyptic periods. Given that living humans can survive for long periods of time in a well-prepared (and fortified) shelter and Type 1 zombies will have a very limited lifespan, we believe that society can "run out the clock" on the apocalypse.

RUN

Regardless of a properly confirmed diagnosis of zombie type or subtype, the first thing one should do is take shelter. If you are already well stocked with food, water and medicine, then shelter should take precedence over obtaining weapons. If you are wholly unprepared when the outbreak begins, take as little time as possible to gather survival materials and get inside. If the roads are too dangerous due to accidents, traffic jams or military/law enforcement vehicles, then you may have to stay where you are, whether it is in a shopping mall, airport or at your place of school or work.

In a Type 1 zombie outbreak, the resurrected zombies will be slow and have limited attacking power. Getting to safety during a Type 1 outbreak should be quite easy since the zombies can be effortlessly outmaneuvered.

HIDE

Once you have established your shelter, it's best to settle in and be as quiet as possible. Any errant noise, visual stimuli or odors could attract a zombie that has intact sensation. Although it is hypothesized that the Resurrected Dead will likely have blunted senses at best, we may not know early in an outbreak whether or not this is true. Therefore, it is highly recommended to follow these guidelines:

- Make as little noise as possible. Try to use headphones for listening to communications programming (or watching Netflix). Keep children occupied and as quiet as possible. For those with babies, good luck. Likewise, bring pets inside the home and keep them fed and occupied so they do not bark or make any kind of noise. This will also protect the pet from being an easy meal for the zombie.

- Keep the lights turned off and do not walk in front of windows. It is best to cover windows so as not to create shadows. This can be done with thick curtains or blinds. If one has a completely uncovered window, a large piece of furniture should be moved in front of it. This also helps prevent curious children or animals that may want to look out of the windows.

- Do not build fires in the fireplace, as the smoke would be like a beacon to the zombies. Likewise, outdoor fires are extremely risky due to the production of smoke and bright flickering light.

These simple steps will prevent visual, auditory and olfactory stimuli from attracting unwanted attention. If zombies remain unable to gain nourishment and are chronically exposed to the elements, they will perish in fairly short order. This is why the final and most important step in the strategy is to WAIT.

WAIT

Under any circumstance of apocalyptic or sub-apocalyptic zombie outbreak, the safest strategy is to merely wait it out. In preparation of this strategy, focus groups revealed that waiting is an unpopular tactic. Americans in particular are looking forward to the apocalypse merely to use up stored ammunition or to get a chance to use the crossbow that's been hanging on their wall with the price tag still attached.

So many citizens prefer not to wait because they believe the zombies will persist until they are neutralized with extreme force. Others believe the time from death to complete decay is too long to merit waiting. But we suggest that complete decay is not the goal. Instead, we believe the time from death to **Effective Decay** is more important. Time of Effective Decay (denoted as t_{ED}) is the degree of decomposition that will render any resurrected corpse ineffective with regards to attacking capacity. This depends on a number of factors, most importantly geography, climate, weather and season during which the outbreak occurs.

Those in warm climates will enjoy a very short t_{ED}. Increased temperature promotes bacterial growth and results in rapid decomposition. With exposure to sunlight, in under 12 hours a freshly resurrected corpse would be melting, with skin falling off and bloating due to gas formation. These features alone will greatly limit the mobility of a corpse. But the main ally to humans in a Type 1 outbreak will be the fly; more specifically, the larvae phase of the fly life cycle: the maggot.

Flies are very efficient in removing dead flesh from the environment. It all begins when the fly senses death by detecting sulfur-containing compounds released in the very early decomposition stage. Flies then lay their eggs on the corpse and those eggs grow into maggots. The maggots do all the heavy lifting with regards to devouring a corpse. Maggot formation can occur in moderate or cool climate and can even occur indoors. It is estimated that in moderate environmental temperatures, maggots can de-flesh corpse in about 7 days after hatching.

But consider that it is not complete defleshing that is necessary to reach t_{ED}; one only needs enough flesh removal to render the corpse's attacking ability ineffective. In a tropical climate, the t_{ED} can be 24 hours or less, especially if maggots extensively devour the muscles of the lower extremities.

The elements also play a role in decomposition and t_{ED}. In areas with heavy rains or wind, corpses will decompose even faster than expected. An example from the world of forensics is when a person dies in a bathtub partially filled with water. The moisture promotes very rapid decomposition and if there are flies present, an immense amount of hungry maggots can quickly deflesh a corpse.

Then there are the animals. Dogs, coyotes, wolves and birds would attack the resurrected dead in search of a meal. The action of animals eating corpses is called **anthropophagy**, which translated means 'the eating of man'. Dogs in particular would relish a fresh tibia, femur or ribs. In rural areas where there are many wild animals and unleashed pets, the corpses would be summarily destroyed before being able to attack.

Considering all factors such as temperature, elements and animal and insect activity, in a warm climate the t_{ED} would be in the 48-96 hour range, an easily survivable interval even for an unprepared citizen. It would be difficult for any resurrected zombie to survive longer than 2 weeks given all the above factors. Although unsightly and terrifying, these zombies will simply decay until reaching t_{ED}. The biggest challenge at that point will be environmental cleanup and triage of bodies and human remains to their final resting place.

The Type 2 Apocalypse: Alive, Aggressive & Extremely Dangerous

The factors that give the living a huge advantage over the Type 1, Resurrected Dead zombies have little effect or relevance on the Type 2 zombies. Type 2 zombies share our human physiology and do not bend to the will of the elements. Our friends the flies and the maggots—the chief architects of our survival of a Type 1 apocalypse—will play no role against Type 2 zombies since they will not have any dead or dying flesh. So this presents a problem because it is no longer the Dead vs The Living, it is The Living vs The Extremely Aggressive Living. These zombies are fast and strong, will attack and won't necessarily eat you, but may chew your flesh off. The so-called Bath Salts Zombie was terrifying enough as an isolated incident; now imagine tens of thousands of afflicted citizens manifesting extreme violent aggression. We may not even be safe indoors.

The Scope of a Type 2 Outbreak

Calculation of the zombie threat is much more difficult with Type 2 zombies. In contrast with Type 1, the underlying cause of the disease is paramount to understanding the threat that we face. Type 1 zombies would likely be a pseudo-metaphysical event in which the cause is nebulous and perhaps unimportant if it is not transmissible. A transmissible agent such as a virus or prion would result in a situation where the only limit to the number of infected would be the size of the population: 7 billion individuals and counting. Many simulations have been reported using epidemiological and statistical computer models, however most of these models assume bite transmission will be the primary means that the infection passes from person to person. As we have established in this text, bite transmission is a poor way for an outbreak to proceed, but some models have indicated this mode of transmission could result in a worldwide apocalyptic threat in short order.

Unfortunately, this is not consistent with reality. The simplicity of bite transmission is excellent for modeling because it is implied that one bite always equals one infection, and there is never a question about who may be infected. The length of the incubation period is not taken into consideration because of the myth of "instant conversion". In an infection that is not transmitted by bite (say, by airborne droplets) and has a variable incubation period, untold numbers of individuals might be walking around infected and shedding the infectious agent for days. This is truly the worst-case scenario and is similar to the model that causes influenza epidemics and pandemics.

Contrary to what has been portrayed in pop culture, not all zombie outbreaks will be an immediate worldwide apocalyptic threat. Most outbreaks of new diseases are initially a slow burn and then develop into an unstoppable monster sometime later. In fact, the worst pandemic of the last 700 years, the 1918 Spanish influenza, did not immediately paralyze society. The virus was spreading in the spring of 1918 and caused the usual amount and severity of flu illness before going dark in the summer. Then the flu resurrected in the autumn of 1918 and spread like wildfire, killing millions upon millions of people at the same time World War I was grinding to its end. The disease began locally, spread to a few different areas and then eventually swept over the face of the earth. The theoretical zombiism pandemic could start as isolated outbreaks, just as the 1918 flu did, before becoming something much bigger.

While not "instantaneous", there are actually many factors in favor of the rapid spread of a new disease. The world has grown smaller in two ways: 1) ease and quickness of long distance travel and 2) overcrowding. A person can now get on a plane in Beijing, China and arrive in Los Angeles in about 12 hours. As such, one person carrying a deadly infection can infect another who was separated by 6,000 miles that same morning. One can only imagine how much worse the 1346 bubonic plague or the 1918 Spanish flu might have been with rapid travel. Together, both diseases killed over a quarter of a *billion* (250,000,000) people with the fastest intercontinental transportation at the time was by boat and depended only on the winds and waves of waterways.

The second big factor is that of overcrowding. In only 100 years the world population grew by 5 billion people from 1918 - 2018. Thus the average population density across the earth has increased. Areas that used to be untouched by man are now bustling cities with high-rises and apartments stacked upon apartments. Very simply put, if people are closer together, the risk of infection increases due to an increased chance of interpersonal contact and sharing of resources. Rising sea levels may put undue stress on coastal cities and villages, forcing hundreds of millions of people further inland, packed closer together. Improvements to health care, sanitation and infrastructure have also produced a situation very favorable for human reproduction and population growth. The Spanish flu killed around 50 million despite many factors against disease transmission; today such an easily transmissible disease might kill 500 million or more.

These are the kinds of numbers we might be facing with a Type 2 apocalypse. While the Type 1 apocalypse is more likely to be a slow-developing event that will not consume the living in short order, the Type 2 disease could spread far and wide in less than a year. This would cause widespread devastation to population numbers and stability of the world in general.

Physical Limits of Type 2 Zombies

Whether the cause is biological or chemical, the physical characteristics that make Type 2 zombies a terrifying threat also provide the limitations that give us a definitive edge over time. Whereas the Type 1 zombies must bow to their external environment, the Type 2 zombies' biggest obstacle to survival will be the internal environment. That is to say, the very substance of the zombie bodies will finally break down under immense physical stress, just as any normal human body would.

A primary determinant for the natural lifespan of these zombies will be dehydration. Consider that a completely unaffected human will perish in about 72 hours without water. Under normal circumstances, the brain of a dehydrated human will sense the loss of water and this triggers a thirst response, which causes us to drink to normalize fluid balance. In the hyperadrenalized/excited delirium state of the zombie, increased sweating and constant movement will result in abundant water loss. If the zombie does not replenish fluids, death could occur in as little as 48 hours. Excited delirium and extreme aggression is at its root an irrational behavior, but would that irrationality override basic physiologic needs such as food and water? This cannot be predicted.

Markedly increased muscular activity (with or without dehydration) can cause muscle breakdown, a condition known as rhabdomyolysis. Such a condition can arise in individuals engaged in physical activities such as marathons or long periods of weightlifting. If severe, death can result from acute kidney failure due to the inability to remove excess muscle proteins from the blood, compromising the kidney. Another effect of cellular breakdown is hyperkalemia, an increased blood potassium (K^+) levels. This occurs because the K^+ ion is primarily localized inside of cells, and breakdown of the cells releases the potassium into the bloodstream. If the concentration of K^+ gets too high, it is well known to produce fatal heart arrhythmias.

Changes to the basic needs of physiology can cause death in zombies that were in perfect health even before infection. Consider that many people that already have significant underlying medical conditions will also be affected by zombiism. For instance, a person with moderate to severe coronary artery disease may have a marked increase in heart rate and blood pressure that could easily produce a heart attack or trigger a fatal arrhythmia. This is similar to what happens with individuals with coronary atherosclerosis who die while engaged in physical activity. A zombie with pre-existing hypertension could easily have a brain hemorrhage due to the sky-high increase in blood pressure that would occur during an attack. The excited state can also produce hyperglycemia (high blood sugar), which in a diabetic zombie could produce a fatal condition known as diabetic ketoacidosis or diabetic coma.

Climate Effects

The effect of climate is another factor that is often forgotten in the portrayal of the zombie apocalypse. The Type 2 zombies are not susceptible to decay due to environmental conditions or the work of maggots, but are susceptible to excesses of temperature and precipitation. An ultra aggressive zombie with excited delirium may already be hyperthermic (increased body temperature) due to problems with temperature regulation in the brain combined with increased muscle metabolism. If the outbreak occurs in an area with already high environmental temperature, then death due to heat stroke becomes a much higher possibility. Dehydration will also develop much more quickly. In a cold climate, the zombie will quickly succumb to hypothermia (core temperature less than 95° F/35° C). Without proper clothing, hypothermia can develop in less than 30 minutes in below freezing temperatures. Many areas of the northern latitudes as well as high altitude mountainous areas have below freezing temperatures and snow for much of the year and are fairly insulated from the effect of worldwide zombiism outbreaks. Certainly, it is the temperate climates that are in the most peril with respect to Type 2 zombies, because is provides an environment most suitable to maximal zombie function and life span.

So how will these living and breathing Type 2 zombies compare to the sluggish, lurching and brain dead (literally) Type 1 Resurrected Dead? Overall, the Type 2 zombies are much more dangerous and capable of attack despite possibly being devoid of truly rational behavior. The following comparisons are made with respect to some of the Type 1 zombie classic myths that were discussed above.

Yes, the Type 2 Zombies Will Find You

While classical zombies likely have poor senses, Type 2 zombies might actually have senses that are more acute than healthy humans. The persistent 'fight or flight' response that is induced by our survival instincts is facilitated by the production and release of epinephrine and norepinephrine (referred to commonly as 'adrenaline') by our adrenal glands. When these chemicals are released, our senses are heightened, just as we would need them to be in a survival situation. As such, Type 2 zombies would likely have increased visual acuity and be more aware of subtle movements. Trying to quietly creep past or outmaneuver a zombie could incite a vicious attack.

Likewise, hearing and sense of smell would both be elevated, so in order to survive the onslaught of these zombies one would need to attract as little attention as possible.

Whereas the Type 1 zombies are easily outsmarted and avoided, the Type 2 zombies would react impulsively and with varying degrees of rationality, making them more difficult to avoid and escape. There may even be rudimentary problem solving ability that the Resurrected Dead could not display. Patients with excited delirium are well known to do anything it takes, regardless of bodily injury, to enter into a secured residence or facility. Many such attacks have been caught on tape, where a person will smash through plate glass with their hands and suffer devastating sharp force injuries but continue to advance, all the while with blood spurting from their wounds. An unreinforced door would not stop a Type 2 zombie. Thus, this will have implications for how you might prepare your shelter. Whereas the Type 1 zombies are weak and relatively unmotivated, the Type 2 zombies will actively try to breach your shelter.

The Type 2 Zombies Will Absolutely Catch You

The notion of speed and maneuverability of a Type 2 zombie is a terrifying reality. The zombie will be incredibly fast and strong due to aggression centers of the brain that are persistently activated. Excited delirium is a condition that results in agitation, super strength and paranoia. Whereas we might exercise and know when to stop to not overexert ourselves, these Type 2 zombies will have no 'off switch'. Even more disconcerting, is that attempts to stop individuals with excited delirium are often futile. There are many reports of such patients suffering grave injuries yet continuing to move and attack. Law enforcement is well aware of the problems associated with this and sometimes it has taken up to a dozen police officers to stop one man. In our experience at autopsy, we have seen individuals take bullets that have passed through the thoracic aorta and the subject continues to run for 2 city blocks before dying. In virtually everyone else, this is an injury that would kill the person where they stood. The zombie may be able to survive such mortal injuries much longer than would be expected for a normal human body. This is in part due to diminished pain reception that the zombie might experience in the excited state. Perhaps more significant would be the persistent high blood pressure of the affected zombie patient. When the heart rate and blood pressure are both markedly elevated, the circulation to the brain is maintained and would allow for higher functions such as running and attacking, at least for a period of time after injury.

The Type 2 Zombie Motive: It's Not Brains

One of the leading questions is whether or not a zombie of any type will try to eat the unaffected human. Again, brains are not the motive of even the strong and agile Type 2 zombie because it is simply too difficult to get inside a human skull. But it is well documented that those involved in attacks with patients suffering from excited delirium often incur multiple bites and even large sections of flesh may be ripped off in the attack. A return to a more primitive mindset in the zombie brain might result in a motive based more on hunger just as an animal in the wild hunts its prey. However, the most troubling thing about the zombie attack motive is that there might not be one at all.

Does Run, Hide, Wait ™ Work During a Type 2 Apocalypse?

Certainly, if the outbreak consists of athletic, aggressive and hyperviolent zombies, you are probably dealing with Type 2 zombiism. In the early days of the outbreak when there are fewer zombies, your best bet for survival will certainly be Run Hide Wait™, but how long would one have to wait in a Type 2 apocalypse? Put another way, what is the lifespan of a patient afflicted with Type 2 zombiism? To make a prediction, we must assume that the chemical-based zombies and the infection-based zombies have essentially the same effect: The brain regions that keep aggression in check are irreversibly damaged.

We also assume that this pathologic effect on the brain will not kill the patient in short order, but instead will result in an activated state in which the limits will be those of human physiology. If the zombie remains nourished both with food and water and the climate is mild, the lifespan could be weeks to months. This would be in a situation in which the zombie does not die of an underlying illness and of course not neutralized by private citizens or law enforcement. The state of persistent activation is a very stressful condition for the human body and it is likely that some underlying condition or physiologic abnormality will fell most zombies within a week. Furthermore, amongst the infectious diseases that could cause zombiism, most would eventually result in the death of the patient as the organism or prion extends into other areas of the brain not involved specifically with aggressive or attacking behavior. For instance, as areas of motor function or the control of breathing might become irreparably damaged, the zombie would be rendered completely ineffective.

The citizen caught in a Type 2 outbreak will have to be more vigilant in reinforcing a shelter, preparing for a long period of waiting and being armed in case a zombie breaches the shelter or if one needs to leave for supplies. So, in the strictest sense, although the Run Hide Wait™ strategy is best suited for a Type 1 apocalypse, it will work in a Type 2 outbreak, with the appropriate modifications.

Non-Infectious Type 2 Zombiism:

Can a Drugs or Chemical Produce a Widespread Outbreak

We have explained before that a chemical or drug could cause Type 2 zombiism and would appear similar to the potentially violent excited delirium seen with methamphetamine, cocaine and cathinones. In this circumstance, the condition would not be communicable but could significantly disrupt society if many people were affected all at once, such as the intentional poisoning of a commonly shared resource like a water supply. The concept of chemical warfare is not new.

In 585 BCE (585 BC), an Ancient Greek medicine man named Nebros advised the Athenian military to poison the water supply of the city of Kirrha, Greece with hellebore. Hellebore is a type of plant that when ingested is toxic to both animals and humans. The soldiers stationed in Kirrha drank the hellebore-tainted water and developed such severe gastrointestinal distress that they were unable to defend the city from siege. This was one of the first chemical warfare attacks on record and was successful in winning the battle and ending the war; such results emboldened future generations for even more nefarious methods. After two thousand years of poisoning men, women and children, the final line was crossed during World War I. Between 1915 and 1918, chemical weapons phosgene, xylyl bromide, chlorine and mustard gases killed nearly 100,000 soldiers and almost 1 million more were severely injured. In 1925, the Geneva Convention outlawed chemical weapons.

Despite this, we know there are rogue governments and terrorist organizations that are not above using unconventional warfare. Should such a plan be enacted with a chemical that causes Type 2 zombiism, the goal would likely be the introduction of chaos into society as opposed to the complete conversion of the population to zombie-like individuals. Only a few hundred intensely aggressive type 2 zombies could completely destabilize a city, especially if the cause was not initially known. If the chemical agent did irreversible damage to key areas of the brain, the "outbreak" could last several days at minimum.

***

The way that we will survive and recover from a zombie apocalypse will depend on the nature (type) and severity of the disease. Beyond the medical implications of an apocalyptic type outbreak, the effects on society are difficult to predict but would be wide ranging. Any type of infectious zombiism would put immense strain on the medical, law enforcement and legal systems. Zombiism would bring unique challenges because of the contagion of extreme violence that would be a primary feature of the disease. Whether the apocalypse consists of a large-scale mass resurrection or small, sporadic outbreaks, the world would undoubtedly experience civil unrest. But this has more to do with the instability of the human psyche in the face of crisis than it does the numerical and physical threats of the zombies themselves. It is more likely that the greatest risk during an apocalyptic event will be rogue militia, hostile governments or terror groups that could seize on the chaos of the moment.

It's important to remember that even the most devastating illnesses have not been able to derail the forward thrust of humanity. The Spanish flu killed tens of millions of people but those that were infected and survived gained immunity to the infection. Within one year of the start of the outbreak, the scourge disappeared from the face of the earth and has never returned. In the time since, the human population has grown by 5 billion people.

We must also consider the possibility that the zombie "apocalypse" may not be an apocalyptic event at all. Outbreaks of the disease may be limited and sporadic like that of the seasonal influenza. Zombiism might simply present as a periodic nuisance that causes a few days of unrest after which we return to life as usual. Admittedly, the resurrection of the dead in a Type 1 zombiism outbreak would raise many scientific and theological questions for debate.

At present time, the causes for zombiism remain theoretical but there are many examples from nature, medicine and chemistry that allow us to imagine how these agents could produce zombiism. The question of whether or not any of the chemical or infectious agents described in this book could rise to the apocalyptic level is unable to be answered at this time. Most disturbing, is that despite our best efforts to predict and prepare for the zombie apocalypse, it may well arise from a force we have never seen, have never anticipated or simply cannot explain once it manifests. But even among the worst-case scenarios, well-prepared humans will (probably) survive the zombie apocalypse.

AFTERWORD:

The Postmortem of a Zombie Thought Experiment

Growing up in a small town in southern Indiana, the risen dead were never far from my mind. Rumors of the world's end always seemed to be swirling in my small community; every year there was a new date for the Apocalypse. When I was about 14 years old, a man carrying a Bible and wearing a long black coat came to the picturesque town square of Paoli, Indiana. With the backdrop of an 1800's-era courthouse and its looming Roman columns, he stood at the south end of the lawn and preached about the End Times. Flanked on both sides by large Civil War cannons, he spoke of a time when the sky would go dark, great calamities would befall us and ultimately, the dead would rise from the grave. So many of these men delivered their sermons but the date for the End of the World always came and went. But this one stuck with me. His delivery was authoritative and his voice boomed with apocalyptic dread.

I was haunted by the imagery he painted for us. I pictured decaying corpses rising from their graves in the rural cemetery where my elderly relatives were buried. I was absolutely and unequivocally convinced that I was in my last year of life on Earth and that soon I would meet my doom. Naturally, I breathed a sigh of relief when the end of the world didn't come on October 18, 1989. Yet because I had been so thoroughly convinced Armageddon was at hand, I was forced to give a lot of thought about death and what it meant both theologically and medically. I immersed myself in medical books to find out more about the body and its anatomical intricacies. I continued to engage in deep reflections about the "how and why" of human disease. Years later, I found myself in medical school, where my thoughts about death and disease were finally translated into action.

As school progressed, I was routinely dealing with cadavers, infectious diseases and terminally ill patients. I was once again forced to face mortality every day, both my own and my patients. Most of the learning in medicine could be considered hypothetical situations of imaginary patients with diseases so rare that one may go an entire career without seeing them. Common things are common, but we prepare for the one in a million patient *just in case*. Hence, the idea about what could cause a sustained zombie apocalypse came to me during my residency training in pathology.

While eating lunch with one of my friends from neurosurgery, I breached the topic of zombiism and we bantered back and forth about what infectious organisms would be most likely to cause such a disease. I kept coming back to a concept that was not well known outside of medical circles: the prion. Just a few years before, the Mad Cow epidemic in the United Kingdom made worldwide news. I pointed out to him that Mad Cow disease had crossed into humans because the food supply became contaminated with the deadly prion, so what was preventing it from happening again? I took it a step further, suggesting a prion disease that uncharacteristically was transmitted easily and acted rapidly. Such a prion would destroy or activate key areas of the brain that deal with extreme aggression and attacking behavior, unleashing a torrent of rabid, vicious humans into the streets. He furrowed his brow and gave a somewhat nauseated look down at the hamburger on his plate and said, "I think I'll become a vegetarian."

The zombie was no longer a graveyard myth to me; it became something very real. If you use just a little imagination and tinker with the principles of infectious disease, the supernatural zombie could jump from the realm of fiction to the real world pretty easily. Because the zombie is both fascinating and terrifying, it has become such a staple of modern horror fiction that the ideas of writers and filmmakers have given us plenty of examples from which to compare zombies and create our own unique conception of them.

There are many concepts in zombiology that are sources of great controversy between both professional and amateur zombiology theorists alike. I have seen well-meaning people almost come to blows during conversations about the nature of zombies. In fact, many of the titans of zombie fiction have become annoyed at attempts to define or overanalyze the scientific aspects of the zombie, often commenting that "the zombies are not the point of the stories so don't focus on their realness or lack thereof". While I agree that we consume stories for the *people* in them, some of us cannot escape our scientific inclinations.

This is not a "buzzkill" approach but instead mere 'thought experiments' about zombie realism. Having been in the midst of countless conversations about shows like *The Walking Dead* and movies such as *Dawn of the Dead* and *28 Days Later*, the topics are rarely about the *people* and more about what kinds of weapons we might use and exactly what in the world caused the outbreak. But the mystery of why or how zombies exist is a large part of their appeal and examination of how they could exist should not diminish the value of these zombie thought experiments.

Regardless of the plausibility of zombie realism, the resurrection of the dead has been a universal theme in myths, legends and religious traditions for thousands of years. It is perhaps a manifestation of the rejection of death's permanence that gives the zombie symbol its longevity. More than anything, the zombie has become a metaphor of the all-consuming nature of our society. Whether it is food, alcohol, drugs or the digital world, we devour our time with mindless activities and no matter how much we consume we never seem to get enough. In the end, we consume ourselves.

Maybe *we* are our own slow-moving zombie apocalypse?

/DLW

Appendix A
Glossary of Terms

Algor mortis: the cooling of the body temperature after death.

Arbovirus: A virus carried by and transmitted by an arthropod.

Arthropod: an invertebrate animal of the large phylum *Arthropoda*, such as an insect, spider or crustacean.

Autolysis: the destruction of cells and tissues by their own enzymes.

Autopsy: a an examination of the body after death, involving evidence collection and surgical dissection. The goal of the autopsy is to determine the cause and manner of death.

Ballistics: the science of projectiles and firearms.

Blowback: the blood and/or tissue fragments that spray in the opposite direction of the entering bullet.

Brain mist: particulates of brain tissue, blood and cerebrospinal fluid that emerge from a high velocity head wound of a zombie.

Bulla: (*plural: bullae*) A fluid-filled blister occurring on the skin after death.

Cadaveric spasm: the instantaneous rigor mortis a body develops due to strenuous activity at the time of death.

Cause of Death: in forensics, the underlying disease process that resulted in the outcome of death.

Effective Decay: the degree of decomposition necessary to render a zombie Ineffective (t_{ED}).

Encephalitis: inflammation or infection of the brain tissue.

Encephalopathy: a disease in which the functioning of the brain is affected by some agent or condition (such as viral infection or toxins in the blood).

Endocannibalism: the eating of the flesh of one's own group or tribe.

Excited delirium: a condition in which the individual suffers from extreme agitation, hyperthermia, paranoia and super strength and speed. Can be drug related, psychiatric or due to type 2 zombiism.

Exocannibalism: the eating of outsiders of the same species.

Iatrogenic: a medical condition or illness resulting from treatment or medical intervention.

Idiopathic: relating to a disease, of which the cause is unknown

Kinetic energy: the energy of movement or motion.

Livor mortis: the settling of blood after death due to gravity.

Manner of Death: the grouping category of the nature of the death. Includes Accident, Homicide, Natural, Suicide and Undetermined.

Martial Law: the suspension of normal law; a government run by military.

Minimum

Safe Distance (MSD): The minimum distance one can be to a zombie target that minimizes infection during a defensive attack by the human.

Mutation: a change in the genetic material of an organism that results in changes in structure and/or function.

Muzzle velocity: the velocity of a bullet (projectile) upon leaving the gun barrel.

Necropsy: the postmortem exam of an animal; animal autopsy.

Patient Zero: the first person to carry a disease in an outbreak of that disease.

Prion:	a portmanteau of the words "protein" and "infection", referring to the infectious protein agent that causes "prion diseases".
Prodrome:	an early symptom indicating onset of a disease or other illness.
Projectile:	the piece(s) of the bullet that leaves the gun when fired.
Radiation:	the emission of energy as electromagnetic waves or as moving subatomic particles, especially high-energy particles which cause ionization.
Range of Fire:	the distance from the muzzle of a gun to the target where the bullet impacts.
Quiescent:	a state of being inactive or dormant.
Sepsis:	an infection within the blood, usually with bacteria or fungus.
Sign:	any objective evidence of disease
Symptom:	any subjective evidence of disease
Temporary Cavity:	the space produced in tissues around a fast-moving bullet.
Type 1 Zombie:	the classical form of the zombie. The walking dead. A resurrected corpse that attacks.
Type 2 Zombie:	the living form of a zombie that may be caused by a biological or chemical agent.
Vascular marbling:	the arborizing skin pattern of blood decomposition seen on the skin surface.
Zombiology:	the study of zombies and the disease of zombiism.

Appendix B
Clinical Zombiism: The PQR Sequence

<u>Stages of Disease: The PQR Sequence</u>

Whether one is #teamResurrectedDead or #teamNewWorld, there are three basic stages of the zombie disease, known as the "PQR Sequence":

1) Prodrome (P)

2) Quiescent State (Q)

3) Reanimation (R)

<u>Prodrome (P):</u>

A **prodrome** is a general medical term that means an early symptom that indicates the onset of disease or illness. When we have a cold or the flu, the prodrome can include nonspecific signs like sore throat, headache or a cough. The typical zombiism prodrome may have a pretty stark beginning, usually with a zombie bite or exposure to some zombie bio-fluids. At the point of exposure, infection is presumed and the prodromal phase will continue with worsening symptoms. There would be severe pain at the site of the bite due to the many cutaneous nerves that are ruptured by the biting force. When such an injury occurs, cells of the immune system pour into the wound in an attempt to stop whatever infectious agent might be present. This also begins the repair process of the wound, and increased blood flow can result in a red, inflamed-appearance.

Because zombiism has not affected modern populations in any significant numbers, humans would have no natural immunity. This could cause the infection to proceed quickly and unabated. The next part of the prodrome would be when the organism replicates itself in both the tissue and the blood. This can produce **sepsis**, a deadly infection of the bloodstream that can rapidly proceed to organ failure and death. Such a severe infection often comes with high fevers and shaking chills.

In zombie pop culture, the prodromal phase can range anywhere from almost zero minutes (Instant Conversion) to a more realistic interval of hours to days. In these cases, the bitten develop a worsening sickness that lasts until clinical death or the Quiescent phase. Bacterial, fungal and viral infections usually take many hours to incubate since the organism must reproduce itself in sufficient numbers to cause infection. In the case of prion-based zombiism, the prodromal phase would likely be longer than typical infections. The prion prodrome would present with neurological and psychiatric symptoms such as depression, hallucinations and mania. The end of the prodrome begins the transition to the next phase: a deep coma that may look like clinical death.

Quiescent Phase (Q)

At the end of the prodromal phase the patient may appear to be slipping into a coma state, similar to that which precedes death in terminally ill patients. A dying patient may take rapid and shallow breaths until the heart slows and then finally stops. **Quiescent** is a word meaning a 'state of being dormant or inactive'. Pop culture depictions have shown quiescent phase to last mere seconds to many hours. In the resurrected dead, the Q phase may be hundreds or even thousands of years. This phase of the zombie sequence may be like a type of hibernation while the brain 're-boots'. There are some ideas about what might occur during the Q phase. This could represent a time for incubation and replication of the causative organism to result in the pathological effects on the brain. Others have suggested this time could actually represent a resolution of the worst stage of the infection, leaving the damaged brain in a permanent zombie state. Regardless of the duration of the Q phase, it ends with the zombie becoming active and entering its most dangerous phase, Reanimation.

Reanimation (R Phase)

The phase of reanimation (R Phase) is the final step in transformation from human to zombie. As the Quiescent phase ends, the transformation is complete and this will be the time when the zombie is most dangerous because the zombie will have the most energy and physical ability to attack bystanders. The R phase will then last a widely variable amount of time depending on zombie type. A Type 1 zombie (Resurrected Dead) R phase will last until environmental conditions and decomposition renders the zombie ineffective, also known as the "time to effective decay". Among Type 2 (New World) zombies, the reanimation phase will last until the zombie dies naturally, is neutralized, quarantined or receives treatment. Based on the most likely agents of zombie transformation, it is highly unlikely that the infected would undergo spontaneous resolution of the disease without severe long-term complications.

In the setting of treatment or observation of a potential zombie, the PQR sequence will help in understanding and classifying the zombie type. The key element is the Q phase. If during Q phase, all signs of life disappear, then the zombie must be a Type 1, Resurrected Dead zombie. If during the Q phase the patient maintains signs of life including vital signs, this is diagnostic of a Type 2 infectious zombie.

Exceptions

The chemical or drug-based Type 2 zombies do not follow the classic PQR sequence because the underlying causative agent is chemical and not infectious. Thus, the prodrome (P phase) would merely be the early changes associated with the drug intoxication. With the various drugs that can cause excited delirium or extreme aggression there would likely be no Q phase because there is no basis for the patient to lose consciousness then become active. Without a defined Q phase, there is no Reanimation (R) phase.

Appendix C
Zombiism Nomenclature

<u>Zombie Clinical Syndromes: DEAD, UNDEAD and PDDA</u>

As is the case with so much in science and medicine, acronyms for diseases are common but are often misleading or confusing, especially in this time of great flux in the field of zombiology. The original designation of the condition proposed by Mecklenberg in 1869 was *morsus nex* (Latin; 'the bite of death') and held on well into the mid-1900s. Since then there have been many different iterations of how to name the zombie condition. Some of these disease names were proposed for the World Health Organization (WHO), and despite their rejection can still be found in use. The acronyms DEAD and UNDEAD were proposed by the Hoffman group in 1983 and were initially popular in media, but were found to be confusing by the general public.

The DEAD stands for the '**D**egenerative **E**ncephalopathy **A**ggression **D**isease' and refers specifically to those zombies that truly rise from death to attack humankind. These are Type 1 zombies and are subject to all physical forces of decomposition once reanimation occurs. The UNDEAD stands for the '**U**ndifferentiated **D**egenerative **E**ncephalopathy **A**ggression **D**isease' and refers to the living Type 2 zombies. The term Undifferentiated was added because many of the possible infectious and chemical causes of zombiism that can present with the same clinical symptoms. Because of the generality associated with the word 'dead' these descriptors were not formally adopted and are mainly of academic interest. As such, our group has worked tirelessly on the classification and proper disease naming of living zombies. We have proposed the disease now be called the **Progressive**

Degenerative Disease of Aggression (PDDA). PDDA is a more modern and descriptive clinical interpretation of New World zombiism, eschewing terms that relate only to the state of being dead or not. **P**rogressive means the disease gets worse as time goes on. **D**egenerative refers to the breakdown of the brain and the body. **A**ggression is the defining characteristic of the zombie. Using this new term will also help avoid the dehumanization of those with the disease, although we understand it may take some time for PDDA to be widely accepted. We have submitted the term to be evaluated by the 2020 WHO Congress on Emerging Infectious Diseases.

Acknowledgements

Very Special Thanks

M., S. and J.

Special Thanks

To friends and family and social media followers, without which publishing this book would have been impossible. Some of these followers' names appear in the book as submitted to me, although not all were able to appear in the text. Thank you to Allison, Amigo, Anita, Baloiu, Bermudez, Carey, Chávez, Commander, Corder, De Nada, Drake, Ellison, Fingado, Herrera, Goede, Goffin, Guoan/Blanchette, Hoffpauir, Johnson, José, Karli, Kunzler, Laasasenaho, Landos, Lara/Rachel, Luke, Meek, Moctezuma, Monteiro, Sarah Munger, Natalia, Niola/Barth, Norek, Paliashchuk, Pence, Pizzimenti, Rodrigues dos Santos, Schatz, Shilonosova, Speake, Steinbacher, Sterne, M. Tarlton, Tuma/Debreczeny, Turk, Unfred, Felicia Valadez, Naomi Vega, Vicks, Weidenkeller. If I somehow forgot someone, I'll put you in the next book.

Thanks

Our zombiology research group is comprised of Dr. Rolfe Aldwin (clinical medicine), Dr. Elna Wilford (infectious disease specialist) and Dr. Darin L. Wolfe (forensic pathologist) and their staff.

Thank

If you want to learn more about medicine, disease or pathology, please follow @anatomy_and_the_dead at Instagram.

Printed in Germany
by Amazon Distribution
GmbH, Leipzig

16069853R00101